PRACTI
YOUR
ENGLISH

by
C. E. WOOD

ROBERT GIBSON : PUBLISHER
17 Fitzroy Place, Glasgow G3 7SF

FOREWORD

THIS BOOK is a comprehensive collection of exercises in the essentials of the English language. It provides intensive practice in correct speech and writing and is suitable both for class use and for self-testing before examinations.

Working through the exercises will correct grammatical mistakes, extend vocabulary and test reading comprehension. It will also ensure familiarity with a wide range of useful phrases and typical English forms of expression.

The practice provided in these elements of the language will promote ready comprehension of both the written and the spoken word and will help develop confidence and fluency in speech and writing.

The book may be used either independently for the purpose of assessing progress and attainment or as a supplement to *The New First Aid in English* (also published by Robert Gibson and Sons). In the Analysis of Exercises on pages 4 and 5 the column headed 'N.F.A.' shows the pages in that book where further examples, often with explanations, may be found in *The New First Aid in English*.

ISBN 0 7169 4034 5

INFORMATION CORRECT TO 1984

Printed in Great Britain by
Martin's The Printers Ltd., Berwick upon Tweed

ACKNOWLEDGMENTS

We value highly the permission to include copyright material and are happy to put on record our indebtedness for extracts from:—

I FLY THE ATLANTIC, by V. E. Mearles, by permission of Sir Isaac Pitman & Sons Ltd.

THE ASCENT OF EVEREST, by Sir John Hunt, by permission of the Author and Messrs. Hodder & Stoughton Ltd.

BARON VON MUNCHAUSEN, by Brian Robb, by permission of Messrs. Hutchinson & Co. (Publishers), Ltd.

THE ARM OF THE LAW, by G. A. Campbell, by permission of the Author and Oxford University Press.

THE SILENT WORLD, by J. Y. Cousteau, by permission of the Author and Messrs. Hamish Hamilton Ltd.

THE IMPOSSIBLE ADVENTURE, by A. Gheerbrant by permission of the Author and Messrs. Victor Gollancz Ltd.

MAINLY ABOUT ANIMALS, by permission of Harper Cory Publications Ltd.

THE TEACHERS' WORLD, by permission of The Teachers World and Schoolmistress.

JACK O' THE INKPOT by Algernon Blackwood from THE EDUCATION OF UNCLE PAUL by permission of the Author's Trustee and Messrs. A. P. Watt & Son.

3

ANALYSIS OF EXERCISES

EXERCISE 1

(A) Write your name in full; SURNAME first followed by
CHRISTIAN NAME.
Write down your address as fully and correctly as you can.
Now write the name and address of your school.
What is your date of birth?

(B) *Complete the* PLURALS:—

Singular	Plural	Singular	Plural
loaf	loaves	child	....
book	....	mouse	....
sheep	....	half	....
knife	....	leaf	....
lady	....	orange	....
city	....	woman	....

(C) *Change* ALL THE SINGULARS *into* PLURALS:—
The mouse ran into the house.
The knife was open.
The horse was running into the stable.
The child cried because it was hurt.

(D) *Change* ALL THE PLURALS *into* SINGULARS:—
The men found the boots in the gardens.
The ladies took the loaves into the kitchen.
The children thought their toys were broken.
There are cinemas and factories in the towns.

(E) *Choose the correct word from the brackets*:—
The boy has (ate, eaten) an apple and (drank, drunk)
some milk.
John has (took, taken) his toys to his bedroom.
He (saw, seen) the dog run to its kennel.
Mrs. Smith has (spoke, spoken) to Jim about what he
(done, did).
Our kitten (come, came) home yesterday.

EXERCISE 2

(A) *Complete this table of masculines and feminines*:—

Masculine	Feminine	Masculine	Feminine
man	woman	....	duchess
....	girl	....	vixen
....	queen	....	aunt
father	....	prince	....
....	wife	actor	....

(B) *Change* ALL *masculine into* FEMININES:—

The man took his son to the cinema.
The bull ran across to the colt.
The emperor greeted the actor.

(C) *Write* ALL *singulars as* PLURALS:—

He had a knife in his desk.
The lady nurses her baby.
The child took the box to the chief.

(D) *What are the* PLURALS *of these words?*

sheep	....	leaf	....
wife	....	army	....
tooth	....	woman	....
ox	....	fly	....
potato	....	hoof	....

(E) *There are mistakes in these sentences. Rewrite the sentences correctly*:—

I cannot see it nowhere.
There are a lot of lakes in Switzerland.
I cannot write no more.
He thought the girl done it.
I seen the man climb through the window.
He didn't learn nothing.
Give me them oranges.
They have did it again.

EXERCISE 3

(A) *Write down the* PLURALS *of these singulars*:—

Singular	Plural	Singular	Plural
navy	....	day	....
calf	....	knife	....
life	....	garage	....
root	....	chief	....
brush	....	piano	....
glass	....	reef	....

(B) *Write down the* FEMININES *of these masculines*:—

bull	....	uncle	....
bridegroom	....	nephew	....
master	....	wizard	....
hero	....	bachelor	....

(C) *Write down the names of the* PARENTS *of*:—

a cygnet	....	a lamb	....
a kitten	....	a gosling	....
a duckling	....	a foal	....

(D) *Where would you expect these people and animals to* LIVE?

a king	....	a horse	....
a vicar	....	a dog	....
a man	....	a pig	....
a soldier	....	a rabbit	....

(E) *Choose the correct word from the brackets*:—

He asked me if you (were, was) my friend.
They (wasn't, weren't) the books for which I asked.
It looks as though everybody (have, has) gone home.
The man had (threw, thrown) the purse away.

(F) *Write down words which you think mean* THE SAME AS:—

repair	....	halt	....
commence	....	difficult	....
sufficient	....	circular	....
roam	....	wealthy	....

9

EXERCISE 4

(A) *Put the most suitable* GROUP TERMS *in the blank spaces*:—
His whole *herd* of cattle was lost.
The vicar preached to a large ....
At the farm, I saw—
a .... of sheep, a .... of cattle, a
.... of bees, a .... of geese and I
played with a .... of pups.

(B) *Complete this passage*:—
The vicar is lucky to live in a .... while the
monk lives at the .... The soldier in his ....
and the convict in the .... are not so free to do
as they like. Perhaps the pig in his ...., or the
spider in his ...., is the happiest of all.

(C) *Complete the following*:—
A negro woman is called a ....
A young swan is known as ....
The plural of shelf is ....
A .... is a male goose.
A female horse is called a ....
The feminine of hero is ....
A .... is a male sheep.

(D) *What do we call*:—
a home with all the rooms on the ground floor?
....
a place where motor cars are stored? ....
a room at the top of a house just under the roof?
....
carrots, cabbages, potatoes and turnips? ....
people who sing together? ....

(E) *Write down the* OPPOSITES *of these words*:—
entrance	....	lost	....
bitter	....	up	....
danger	....	over	....

EXERCISE 5

(A) *Complete the following:*

"The night was as black as . . . . The detective who was as bold as . . . . and as cool as a . . . . walked along as steadily as a . . . . He was a tall man, as thin as a . . . . , but as hard as . . . . and as strong as an . . . . Although it was as . . . . as ice that night, he wore no gloves. He reached the house and climbed the pipe as easily as . . . . Once inside, he worked as quickly as . . . . "

(B) *Correct the following sentences:*—
There is four books on the table.
He came home as quick as he could.
John has broke his leg.
This jacket is wore out.
A man and his dog was at the corner.

(C) *Write down the* PLURALS *of these words:*—

party	. . . .	tomato	. . . .
baby	. . . .	monkey	. . . .
fairy	. . . .	eye	. . . .
foot	. . . .	penny	. . . .
box	. . . .	shoe	. . . .

(D) *What are the* MASCULINE *of the following?*—

mistress	. . . .	widow	. . . .
nun	. . . .	niece	. . . .
madam	. . . .	duchess	. . . .
heroine	. . . .	filly	. . . .
headmistress	. . . .	mare	. . . .

(E) *Complete the following collections:*—

an . . . . of soldiers.   a litter of . . . .
a . . . . of sheep.   a bouquet of . . . .
a . . . . of books.   a crew of . . . .
a . . . . of grapes.   a swarm of . . . .
a . . . . of singers.   a chest of . . . .

11

EXERCISE 6

(A) *Complete these sentences with suitable words*:—
   Your book is different .... mine.
   Where .... you yesterday, Tom?
   The boy stood up and .... a lovely song.

(B) *Write down the* PLURAL *forms of these words*:—

man-of-war	....	piano	....
son-in-law	....	fox	....
deer	....	watch	....

(C) *Write down the* MASCULINES *of these feminine words*:—

actress	....	abbess	....
bride	....	authoress	....
stewardess	....	cow	....
sister	....	duck	....

(D) *Choose the* ONE *word from the brackets which means the same as the word in capitals*:—

RAISE	....	(repair, lower, push, lift)
DISCOVER	....	(hide, speak, find, try)
TIMID	....	(bold, strange, afraid, kind)

(E) *Write down* ONE WORD *which means the same as*:—
   a man who lives for nothing but money. ....
   the way by which everyone is supposed to
      go out. ....
   to bring back to mind. ....

(F) *Select the word from the brackets which* RHYMES *with the word in capitals*:—

BEAN	....	(here, neat, seen, peel)
MEAT	....	(meal, heal, heat, peas)
SILK	....	(silt, film, gilt, milk)
PAIR	....	(paid, dare, sail, maid)

(G) *Correct the three words which should have capital letters*:—
   tom goes to school in glasgow, the largest city in scotland.

(H) *Write down the* OPPOSITES *of these words*:—

asleep	stop	alive ....
push	nephew	full ....
love	punish	sweet ....
	junior	

EXERCISE 7

(A) *Complete the following*:—

the ...... croaks.	the lion ....
the .... purrs.	the duck ....
the ...... bleats.	the cock ....

(B) *Choose the correct words from the brackets*:—
     as dry as a (scone, bone, biscuit).
     as like as (two peas, two q's, two bees).
     as pleased as (Judy, Punch, Tom).
     as wise as an (ostrich, fox, owl).

(C) *Complete these phrases*:—

a forest of	a regiment of ....
as .... as a berry.	as cold as ....
a .... of sheep.	as fit as a ....

(D) *What is the word* OPPOSITE IN MEANING *to*:—

friend..........	strong?	everywhere? .....
land?	straight?	beautiful? ....

(E) *Write down words which are* SIMILAR IN MEANING *to*:—

courage........	difficult	glance ....
purchase	rapid	halt ....

(F) *What do these abbreviations mean?*
     a.m........ p.m........ Dr. .... G.P.O. ......

(G) *Write suitable words where there are blanks*:—
     Boy is to Girl as .... is to Woman.
     High is to Low as .... is to Down.
     Uncle is to .... as Aunt is to Niece.
     Wrist is to Arm as .... is to Leg.
     Arrow is to Bow as .... is to Rifle.

(H) *Where are*:—

bees kept?..............   fruit trees grown?.......
films shown?...........   motor cars kept? ....
grapes grown? ....   plays acted? ....
birds kept? ....   ships unloaded?........

EXERCISE 8

(A) *Write these sets of five words in order of size, starting with the* SMALLEST—

    cow, cat, elephant, sheep, mouse.

    ....

    city, town, country, continent, village.

    ....

    ocean, river, spring, stream, sea.

    ....

(B) *Write suitable words in the blank spaces*:—

    Soldier is to .... as sailor is to navy.
    Wheel is to spoke as ladder is to ....
    Here is to there as .... is to that.

(C) *Write these abbreviations in full*:—

Ave. ....   St. ....   Gdns. ....
Mr. ....   Rd. ....   B.C. ....

(D) *Supply suitable words for the blank spaces*:—

Punch and ....   as fresh as a ....
free and ....   a crew of ....
as old as the ....   a bouquet of ....
as fit as a ....   as easy as ....

(E) *Change these words into their* PLURALS:—

thief..........   dwarf ....   scissors ......
leaf ....   key ....   cargo ....
shelf ....   wolf ....

(F) *What do we call the* YOUNG *of the following animals?*

cow ....   owl ....   wolf ....
swan ....   stag ....   horse ....
seal ....   toad ....

(G) *Supply the most suitable "sounding" words*:—

the .... of corks.   the throb of an ....
the .... of a whip.   the slam of a ....
the .... of a rifle.   the .... of feet.

(H) *Correct the following sentences*:—

He couldn't remember nothing.
John done his sums well.
She could not come no quicker.
Your painting is different to mine.

EXERCISE 9

(A) *Place the apostrophe in its correct position in these words*:—

Im, didnt, cant, wouldnt, wasnt, isnt.

(B) *Write down the* OPPOSITES *of these words*:—

early ....   enemy ....   in ....
sometimes ....   long ....   over ....
up ....   black ....   same ....
                to ....

(C) *Select the correct word from the brackets*:—

The (nights, knights) were dressed in armour.
The wreck was marked by a (buoy, boy).
The boys (wasn't, weren't) very good at football.
One of the (rings, rungs) of the ladder was broken.
The confectioner sold delicious (sweets, potatoes).
I bought my spectacles at the (surgeon's, optician's).
We looked in a (magazine, directory) to find the telephone number.
I need a new (pair, pear) of shoes.
The masculine of vixen is (calf, cow, fox).
The tea was placed in the (caddy, scuttle).

(D) *Complete the following phrases*:—

as happy as a ....   as thin as a ....
as poor as a ....   as proud as a ....
as right as ....   as brave as a ....

(E) *Put in the capital letters where you think necessary*:—
new york is the largest city in america, but washington is
the capital.

(F) *Write down words which you think are* SIMILAR IN
MEANING *to the ones given*:—

coarse	....	imitate	....
commence	....	odour	....
valour	....	prohibit	....
annually	....	protect	....
correct	....	vacant	....

EXERCISE 10

(A) *Write down the* PLURALS *of these words*:—
workman........ material ...... solo..........
dictionary....... echo .... county........

(B) *Write* ONE *word which conveys the meaning of each
phrase*:—
Cheering and clapping.   ....
The highest point of a mountain.   ....
Someone who is watching a game.   ....
A child whose parents are dead.   ....
The time between sunset and darkness.   ....

(C) *What do we call*:—
trams, buses, cars, carts, carriages?   v..........
a house with all rooms on the ground floor? b..........
geese, ducks, chickens and turkeys?   p..........
sweets, candy and chocolate?   c..........
carrots, cabbages, potatoes, etc.?   v..........

(D) *Make the* OPPOSITES *of these words by adding something
to the beginning of the word, i.e. by adding a "prefix."*
fortunate....... *polite*.......... *convenient* ......
possible........ *wrap* .... *do*..............

16

(E) *Make* OPPOSITES *to these words by adding something to the* END *of the word, i.e. a "suffix," or by altering the end of the word*:—

careful...............   cheerful..............

useful................   selfish ....

(F) *Write down the* GENERAL WORD *given to each set of things*:—

Ruby, diamond, sapphire	....
Cousin, aunt, uncle	....
Chair, table, wardrobe	....
Water, milk, vinegar	....
Coal, iron, gold, silver	....

(G) *Answer these by using* ONE *word for each*:—

What do we call—

a place where apples are grown?   ....

a place where birds are kept?   ....

a man who is employed to drive a car?   ....

Ev......... means to "turn into vapour."

The opposite of "deep" is ....

A place where railway lines meet is called a ....

O.......... means to "leave out."

EXERCISE 11

(A) *Complete this passage with suitable words*:—

"The man who was as .... as a berry, picked up the heavy sack as easily as .... The wind was as cold as ...., but he was as hard as .... and he whistled as happily as a .... while walking along the narrow lane."

(B) *Write down the* PLURALS *of these words*:—

eye............   dye ....   shoe............…..

Negro ....   glass ....   gas.............

(C) *Correct this sentence by adding the four capital letters required*:—

mrs. brown took jimmy to london to buy new shoes.

(D) *Write down the* OPPOSITES *to these words*:—
entrance .... last............ like.............
sweet..........: possible........ appear..........

(E) *Put these words into* DICTIONARY *order*:—
      bear, biscuit, bison, beetroot, beer.

(F) *Write down words* SIMILAR IN MEANING *to those given*:—
wealthy........ fall............ aid.............
remedy .... broad.......... circular ....

(G) *In the following list of words, one word seems out of place. Choose the word which you think is wrong*:—
      coat, hat, gloves, curtains, pullover.
      needle, pin, scissors, thimble, spoon.
      saw, plane, chisel, hammer, plate.

(H) *Complete these sentences with suitable words*:—
The boy was ashamed .... what he had done.
John took great pride .... his handwriting.
The dog had been lost .... Thursday.
You must hurry home .... school.
I agreed .... my mother that it was cold.
The word which means "not allowed" is ....
At the service, the clergyman preached to a large
....
Read the question and then write your ....

EXERCISE 12

(A) *Correct the following sentences*:—
Tom was the biggest of the twins.
The best team won the game.
Our house was the comfortablest in the road.

(B) *Complete these sentences by using the correct tense of the words "rise" and "raise."*:—
When he met the lady he .... his hat.
I saw him .... from his seat.
Yesterday the boy .... at seven o'clock.
She tried to .... the lid.
The sun had .... in the sky.

18

(C) *Rewrite these jumbled words to form correct sentences*:—

fur Peter cat the a has thick of coat.

....

warmer fly The lands to swallows.

....

(D) *Using the words "lie," "lazy" or "had lain," complete the following*:—

I will .... down and rest.

The kitten .... playing on the floor.

The patient .... on his back for six months.

(E) *Complete these phrases*:—

As penalty is to reward, so ancient is to ....

As praise is to blame, so innocent is to ....

As appear is to disappear, so possible is to ....

As weary is to weariness, so cool is to ....

(F) *Substitute the word from the brackets which is similar in meaning to the word in* CAPITALS:—

It became necessary to ABANDON (dock, leave, steer) the ship.

His work was ACCURATE (neat, quick, correct).

It was a big BLUNDER (mistake, honour, privilege) to invite him to the party.

(G) *Write down words* OPPOSITE *in meaning to*:—

ugly .... lazy .... contented ....

calm .... horizontal ...... cruel ....

(H) *Select the word which does not belong to each group*:—

bear, wolf, fox, robin.

house, flat, train, cottage.

frock, jacket, chair, overcoat.

cotton, satin, wool, dress.

plate, saucer, spoon, cup.

19

EXERCISE 13

(A) *Put the apostrophe in these words*:—
   isnt, theyll, youre, oer, weve, theres.

(B) *Correct these sentences*:—
   George was the heaviest of the two.
   The left shoe was the cleanest of the pair.
   Of the two, I like George best.
   The joiner cut the thinnest end of the wedge.
   "Do not walk so slow," said Mother.

(C) *Choose the correct word from the brackets*:—
   Each of the children (have, has) a toy.
   Everyone of us (know, knows) who did it.
   None of the aeroplanes (was, were) repaired.

(D) *Complete these sentences by inserting suitable preposi-
   tions*:—
   The gardener was an authority .... flowers.
   His car differs .... mine in its colouring.
   The school was proud .... the pupil's success.
   Janet took great pride .... her appearance.

(E) *A* BOOKLET *is a small* BOOK. What names are given to the
   smaller forms of:—
   a hill? ....   a statue?............
   a tart? ....   a river? ....

(F) *What do we call*:—
   a hole made in the tyre of a bicycle? ....
   a place where beer is made? ....
   a room in which an artist paints? ....
   the place where birds are housed? ....
   the room where books are housed? ....
   an unmarried woman? ....
   a person who plays a game for the love of it? ....
   a native of Scotland? ....

20

(G) *Complete the following*:—
        as brown as a ....
        as .... as a pancake.
        a .... of whales.
        rich is to poor as ancient is to ....
        coal is to .... as tea is to caddy.
        the police placed the man under ....
        the .... of metal.
        the .... of bells.

EXERCISE 14

(A) *Complete the following sentences*:—
        The fright made Joan as white as a ....
        After a good night's sleep, I felt as fresh as a ......
        She came back from her holiday as fit as a ....
        The greedy man was as fat as a ....
        The old man walked as slowly as a ....

(B) *What do you associate with these names*:—
Bakery?........ School?........ Bat?............
Football? ...... Tyre?.......... Jet? ....

(C) *Write down the* PLURALS *of these words*:—
mouse .... story .... wolf............
halo........... alley .... dwarf...........

(D) *Write down the* MASCULINES *or* FEMININES:—
buck and ...., ram and ...., lad and ....,
.... and mare, ... and nun, ... and duck.

(E) *Write down the* OPPOSITES *of these words*:—
few........... exit .... nowhere ....
far .... buy .... dangerous ....

(F) *Supply words with the same or nearly* THE SAME MEANING
as the words given:—
infirmary....... caress .... weep ....
vanish .... spring .... relate...........

(G) *Make these words into their* OPPOSITES *by using prefixes*:—

> e.g. usual—*un*usual.

fortunate....... honest........ distinct ....
sense.......... appear........ able ....

(H) *Look at these five phrases*:—
safe and sound; out and out; head and shoulders; rack and ruin; thick and thin.
They are well-known phrases and you are to fit them correctly into these five sentences:—
Through foolishness he went to ....
She is .... taller than her brother.
The ship reached harbour ....
The man was an .... rascal.
The boys would follow their leader through ....
....

EXERCISE 15

(A) *What do you call the place where*:—
doctors receive their patients? ....
fish are kept? ....
people are buried? ....
plays are acted? ....
orphans are looked after? ....

(B) *Complete these phrases*:—

as sharp as a ....   as good as ....
as .... as Punch.   as easy as ....
as .... as the hills.   as proud as a ....
as .... as a new pin.   as silent as the ....

(C) *Complete the following*:—
Foot is to Man as .... is to Horse.
Tear is to Sorrow as Smile is to ....
Food is to Hunger as Drink is to ....
.... is to Cold as Seldom is to Often.

(D) *Supply words* SIMILAR IN MEANING *to*:—
abandon .... abundant....... lofty............
fatigue......... promptly....... circular ....

(E) *Finish these phrases*:—
To let the cat ....
.... out of a mole-hill.

(F) *Choose from amongst the words in brackets the* OPPOSITE
of the first word and write it down:—
Hard (fixed, soft, compact).
Deny (refuse, request, believe, concede).
Love (despise, admire, hate).
Succeed (despair, weep, fail, abandon).
Obstinate (fixed, compliant, good).
Correct (indifferent, bad, stupid, wrong).
Refuse (grant, lend, assist, help).

(G) *Complete these* PROVERBS:—
It's no use crying ....
There's no smoke ....
Every cloud has ....

(H) *What do we mean by*:—
"putting one's shoulder to the wheel"?
....
"coming off with flying colours"?
....
"a storm in a teacup"?
....

EXERCISE 16

(A) *Choose the correct word from the brackets*:—
Every orange (was, were) wrapped in silver paper.
One of the players (has, have) been hurt.
Each member (have, has) the right to vote.
It looks as though everybody (have, has) gone home.
Not one of the eggs (have, has) been hatched.

(B) *Complete these phrases with suitable words*:—

the .... bleats.   the pealing of ....
the .... croaks.   the beat of a ....
the .... gibbers.   the shuffling of ....
the .... drones.   the blast of an ....

(C) *Complete this passage, using suitable words*:—
"In spite of a strong wind, the telegraph pole was as steady as a .... George, as agile as a ...., soon clambered up the pole and, keeping cool as a ...., he began to repair the wires."

(D) *Insert the capital letters and punctuate this sentence*:—
jim said i am going out for a walk

(E) *Select that word from the brackets that* RHYMES *with the word given*:—

stain ....   (tear, live, cane).
bear ....   (stair, rear, cheer).
mood ....   (steed, food, toad).
rein ....   (rain, mean, bean).
cheer ....   (scare, pear, fear).

(F) *Write down the* OPPOSITES *of these words*:—

win .... profit.......... broad...........
happy .... float.......... deep...........

(G) *Correct the following sentences*:—
The train entered the station very slow.
The aeroplanes had flew over the town.
The man come in to the shop to buy tobacco.
The best boxer won the bout.
John had laid in bed during the morning.

EXERCISE 17

(A) *Choose the correct word from the brackets*:—
Mary and (I, me) saw a ship on the horizon.
The wild creature snarled at my sister and (I, me).
He asked the stranger (whence, though) he came.

Neither John (or, nor) James was present.
She is not as old as (I, me).

(B) *Complete these sentences with the appropriate prepositions:—*
  That man is an authority .... books.
  His opinion differs .... mine.
  He was angry .... me.
  She complained .... a cold.
  He was regarded .... a fine footballer.

(C) *Complete the following sentences:—*
  Troops which fight on foot are called in............
  The opposite of "persuade" is ....
  The sound horses make is called ....
  The feminine of "hero" is ....
  A .... is a native of Denmark.
  A young moth is called a ....
  We call a young salmon a ....
  A large number of wolves together is called a ......
  The plural of "chief" is ....
  The masculine of "widow" is ....

(D) *Write the word in the brackets which is* SIMILAR IN
  MEANING *to the word in capitals:—*
  PURCHASE   (win, buy, sell).
  JUST   (fair, fail, certain).
  CONCEAL   (pretend, hide, show).
  TRANSPARENT   (clear, misty, heavy).
  PROHIBIT   (allow, persuade, forbid).

(E) *Complete each sentence with a word formed from the
  word in capitals:—*
  APPLAUD.   The actor was greeted with loud a ....
  ACT.   His a .... was a brave one.
  DEPART.   Our d... was arranged for the morning.
  CONCLUDE.   The choir sang a jolly song in c ......
  EXPLAIN.   An e.... of the crash was given to the
              judge.

25

EXERCISE 18

(A) *Write down* ONE *word which means* THE SAME AS THE WORDS IN ITALICS:—

A boy who is *always on time* ....

A ring *worth a large sum of money*. ....

A story *that makes you laugh*. ....

A boy *who does what he is told*. ....

A castle *which is very old*. ....

An explorer *who is well known*. ....

(B) *Choose* ONE OR MORE *of the words from the brackets which makes the phrase correct*:—

As devoted as a   (lion, mother, master).

As graceful as a   (swan, soldier, March hare).

As happy as a   (president, king, emperor).

As clean as a   (new broom, new penny, new pin).

As quiet as a   (mouse, child, chicken).

As plain as a   (Jane, pikestaff, maid).

(C) *There are errors in* TWO *of the following sentences. Re-write them correctly*:—

We had just began to do it.

The boy lived in a small house.

Tom chose the larger of the three apples.

Mary's doll was beautifully dressed.

(D) *Write down the* OPPOSITE *of the word in italics*:—

He is *seldom* late for school. ....

Manor Road is a *private* road. ....

Mary is Jane's *junior* by two years. ....

Mr. Murray is an *educated* man. ....

James was called a *hero*. ....

(E) *Complete the following*:—

School is to pupils as monastery is to ....

Daffodil is to spring as rose is to ....

Train is to platform as ship is to ....

Ancient is to modern as old is to ....

26

(F) *Put the* TWO *apostrophes in* EACH *of these sentences*:—
A ducks egg is generally dearer than a hens.
Mr. Craigs watch is five minutes slower than Mr.
   Campbells.

(G) *Insert the capital letters and punctuate this sentence*:—
bring roberts cap here the teacher called

EXERCISE 19

(A) *Complete the following Proverbs*:—
Let sleeping .... lie.
Too many .... spoil the ....
Once .... twice ....
Look before ....

(B) *Insert the apostrophe in each of these sentences*:—
The boys caps were placed in a cupboard.
"Bring your books to Johns room," said Mother.
The boys football boots were placed in their lockers.

(C) Make a *noun* from "strong". ....
Make an *adjective* from "sympathy". ....
Give the *opposite* to "poverty". ....
Give the *past tense* of "I tear." ....

(D) *Give words* SIMILAR IN MEANING *to the following*:—
purchase....... feeble .... conceal ....
loyal .... heroic .... moist ....

(E) *"To turn over a new leaf" means*:—
to tidy up the garden; to improve your behaviour; to prune
   the fruit trees.
....
"To get into hot water" means:—
to have a bath; to get into trouble; to call in the plumber.
....

27

(F) *Complete the following by using suitable "sound" words*:—

The donkey .... in the field.

The car stopped with a .... of brakes.

The .... of the owl was heard in the night.

Peace was heralded by the .... of bells.

The .... of a rifle was heard across the park.

(G) *Choose the correct word from the brackets*:—

(Who, Whom) do you think I have (saw, seen)?

(He, Him) it was (whom, who) gave it to (I, me).

(H) *What do we call*:—

a boy who frightens weaker boys? ....

a man who looks after sheep? ....

the low ground between two hills? ....

a ship which can travel below sea level? ....

an instrument for measuring temperature? ....

EXERCISE 20

(A) *Choose the correct word from the brackets*:—

Neither John nor Mary (has, have) a bicycle.

Anybody (is, are) allowed to enter.

I found Bob still (laying, lying) in bed.

(B) *Complete these* PROVERBS:—

A stitch in time ....

A bird in the hand ....

Birds of a feather ....

A rolling stone ....

First come ....

(C) *Write down the* MASCULINES *of these feminines*:—

baroness .... her............ matron..........

heifer.......... sultana .... step-daughter ....

(D) *Insert the apostrophes in each of these sentences*:—

"Where are Marys gloves?"

"Give me my brothers coat."

"I took my friends book to Mr. Turnbulls."

28

(E) *Write down the* SINGULARS *of these plurals*:—
loaves .... dozen .... calves ....
brethren .... feet .... monkeys ....

(F) *Give words* SIMILAR IN MEANING *to these words*:—
velocity .... enemy .... odour ....
prohibit .... interior .... insane ....

(G) *Insert the capital letters and punctuate this sentence*:—
toms father said provided that you are home early you may
  go

(H) *Write down the* OPPOSITES *of these words*:—
success .... arrive .... often ....
sense .... past .... open ....

(I) *Complete this table*:—

tall	taller	tallest
bad	....	....
many	....	....
far	....	....
much	....	....
short	....	....

(J) *Write* ITS *or* IT's *in the appropriate space*:—
  "I believe ... raining," said Robert. "Then I will look
at the rabbit to see if .... all right and that .... hutch
does not leak," replied James.

EXERCISE 21

(A) *Write down the* OPPOSITES *of these words by adding a*
PREFIX:—
correct .... polite .... possible ....
worthy .... direct .... honest ....

(B) *When* EN *is placed at the beginning and sometimes at the
end of certain words, it makes a* VERB. *Make these
words into verbs in this way*:—
deep .... sure .... throne ....
sweet .... trust .... large ....

(C) *In these sentences, the word* ONLY *is incorrectly placed. Put it in its correct position and rewrite the sentences*:—
Ken only has threepence with him.
The poor man only has one finger.
"I only brought my fare," he said.
Jane only took one apple from the basket.

(D) *Complete these* PROVERBS:—
Every cloud has ....
Rome was not built ....
All that glitters ....
All's well that ....

(E) *Select the correct words from the brackets*:—
A person who eats too much is a (miser, glutton, hypocrite).
A lady who sells hats is a (milliner, florist, hosier).
A soldier who rides on horseback is in the (marines, cavalry, infantry).
A wooden shelter made for a dog is a (byre, stable, kennel).
The place where grain is stored is called a (granary, caddy, store).

(F) *Give* ONE *word for each of these*:—
a fertile place in the desert—   o..........
a person who by desire lives alone—   h..........
a person who performs magic—   m..........
a person who looks on the bright side
of things—   o..........
a person who looks on the gloomy side
of things—   p..........
a piece of music for two performers—   d..........
people listening to a concert—   a..........
a person who hides on board ship—   st..........

(G) *Complete this passage*:—
"Jim's mother was angry ..... him for breaking the window. She made him feel ashamed .... himself and said that he must apologise .... Mrs. Mackenzie."

30

EXERCISE 22

(A) *Form* NOUNS, *to fill the blanks, from the word in brackets*:—

The jackal is noted for its c.......... (coward).

Timothy has been delicate from c......... (child).

The Boy Scout was decorated for his h............. (hero).

The police try hard to suppress h........ (hooligan).

(B) *Choose the correct word from the brackets to complete these sentences*:—

A strong .... carried the boat out to sea. (currant, current).

A .... desk is made for two pupils. (dual, duel).

The room was so stuffy that Tony felt .... (feint, faint).

.... is a course served as part of a meal. (desert, dessert).

The sails were made of strong .... (canvas, canvass).

(C) *Choose the correct meaning of these words and complete the sentences*:—

A CALLOUS person is—   hard and unfeeling.
                               very loud voiced.
                               proud and overbearing.

A DELUGE is—   a great swindle.
                       a great flood.
                       a great and pleasant surprise.

A DILIGENT pupil is—   unintelligent.
                               hardworking.
                               very lazy.

(D) *Complete these sentences*:—

The interfering bully was told to mind his own b....s.

The day after Tuesday is W.........y.

In crossing a busy street great care is n........y.

C.O.D. means ....

(E) *Write in* EACH *sentence the* ONE *punctuation mark that is missing*:—
"Is it true that youve sold your penknife?"
"Yes, I sold it last Thursday.
"How much did you get for it"
"I got twenty pence"

(F) *What are the* OPPOSITES *of these words?*—
descended...... lower.......... narrow..........
mean.......... go............. never...........

(G) *Write down* ONE *word which* RHYMES *with each of these words*:—
chair .... eye............ wars............

(H) *What do these abbreviations mean?*—
B.C........ e.g. .... i.e......... U.K. ....

EXERCISE 23

(A) *Rewrite each sentence and underline the* NOUNS:—
Rain stopped play.
The teacher dropped his pen.
The batsman hit his wicket.
Honesty is the best policy.

(B) *Write* PAST *or* PASSED *where appropriate*:—
We strolled .... Buckingham Palace.
Sarah .... the cake to Angela.
Roger was first .... the winning post.
The time .... very quickly.

(C) *Correct the* ONE *punctuation error in* EACH *sentence*:—
"What did it cost to rear him!"
"You did'nt make much profit."
"No, but I had him all summer,"
"I found the boys' pencil in the garden."

(D) *Answer each of these questions by* ONE *word*:—
What should you let sleeping dogs do? ....
What should you do before you leap? ....
What should you make while the sun shines? ....

What does one good turn deserve? ....
What is the mother of invention? ....
What is a good servant but a bad master? ....
What will a rolling stone never gather? ....

(E) *Complete each sentence with the most suitable word:—*
One of the .... of the chain was broken.
The wooden .... of the ladder were rotten.
The .... of the clock swung slowly.
The hard wood blunted the .... of the saw.
One of the .... of the rope was frayed.
Some of the .... of the wheel were broken.

(F) *Choose the correct word from the brackets:—*
"One of your boys (is, are) telling lies."
None of our dogs (were, was) awarded a prize.
She asked me if you (was, were) my friend.
The number of accidents (are, is) increasing.
He did not (accept, except) the gift.
Bob had (eaten, ate) all the toffees.
Of the two, Nora was the (worst, worse) writer.
I shared the toys (among, between) the two boys.

EXERCISE 24

(A) *Complete these sentences with suitable words:—*
After taking my medicine, I felt as right as ....
The soldier was as sturdy as an ....
The tea had become as weak as ....
The gipsy's hair was as black as ....
The man stood as straight as a ....

(B) *Write down the* VERBS *in these sentences:—*
There were no letters on the mat.
I forgot the address.
The top part of the house was burning.
It was bought for ten pence.

(C) *Complete the sentences with the names of* HOMES:—
The rabbit bolted for its ....
There were many bees in the ....
Fred made a .... for his pet rabbit.

There are six pigs in the ....
The lion lay in its ....

(D) *Express by a* SINGLE WORD, *the phrases in italics*:—
This loaf is *not fresh*. ....
He writes to his mother *now and again*. ....
He told them the story *over and over again*. ....
The book is published *once a year*. ....

(E) *Answer these questions*:—
What keeps the doctor away?
What is as good as a mile? ....
Enough is as good as what? ....
How do great minds think? ....

(F) *Correct the following sentences*:—
She is not as old as me.
They sung the same song twice.
The lady sings quite nice.
She took the biggest of the two.
Your answer is different to mine.

(G) *Insert the capital letters and punctuate these two sentences*:—
henry went to bristol to see arthur

....
i have not seen david nor davids books said robert
....

(H) *Complete these expressions*:—
a rolling stone ....   by hook or by ....
to blow one's ....   to make both ends ......
bats in the ....   to turn over a ....
to hit the nail ....   to mind your p's and ....

EXERCISE 25

(A) *Complete these phrases with the names of animals*:—
the .... brays.   the .... hoots.
the .... croaks.   the .... bleats.
the .... barks.   the .... trumpets.

34

(B) *Give the* PLURALS *of these words*:—

spoonful ....   penny ....
mouse-trap ....   bye-law ....
thief ....   city ....
fish ....   manservant............
son-in-law ....   maid of honour ....

(C) *Supply the missing words*:—

as black as ....   as fast as a ....
as meek as a ....   as keen as ....
as brave as a ....   as steady as a ....
as sweet as ....   as safe as ....

(D) *Correct the following sentences*:—

He said that you done it.
She is the biggest of the twins.
He couldn't remember nothing.
She sent it to you and I.

(E) *Write down the* PAST TENSE *of these phrases*:—

I do ....   He writes .....   We bite ....
They fly ....   She freezes ....   You think ......

(F) *By adding a* PREFIX *supply the opposites of these words*:—

possible ....   secure ....   welcome ....
legal ....   legible ....   aware ....

(G) *Name the* HOMES *of the following*:—

tinker ....   gipsy ....   eagle ....
nun ....   horse ....   pigeon ....
bee ....   vicar ....

(H) *Make* NOUNS *from the words in* CAPITALS *and complete these sentences*:—

INTRODUCE. The int....... of the play was made from the stage.

READY. Because of the danger of fire, the buckets of water were in r.........

BROAD. The b ...... of the room was eleven feet.

PROSPER. We wished Mr. Mitchell, "Health, Happiness and P..........."

(I) *insert the capital letters and punctuate the following*:—
do you think said my friend in a whisper that theres a
chance of escape certainly i replied

EXERCISE 26

(A) *Where would you look to find*:—
the address of a person? . . . .
the position of a place? . . . .
the meaning of a word? . . . .
the day and date of the month? . . . .

(B) *Complete these* PROVERBS:—
Let sleeping . . . .
Too many . . . .
Once bitten . . . .
No news is . . . .
One good turn . . . .
A miss is as . . . .

(C) *What do we call*:—
a person who collects fares? . . . .
a metal container for coal? . . . .
a place where flour is made? . . . .
a place where goods are manufactured? . . . .
a fertile place in the desert? . . . .
a hundred years? . . . .

(D) *Write down the* FEMININES *of these words*:—
count . . . . instructor . . . . . . gander . . . .
brave . . . . tutor . . . . bachelor . . . .

(E) *Give the* OPPOSITES *of*:—
success . . . . arrive . . . . often . . . .
poetry . . . . poverty . . . . shallow . . . .

(F) *Where would you buy*:—
fruit? . . . . milk? . . . .
hats? . . . . meat? . . . .
vegetables? . . . . flowers? . . . .
tobacco? . . . . newspapers? . . . .
spectacles? . . . . sweets? . . . .

36

(G) *Which people use the following implements?*
a hoe .... an anvil ....
a palette .... a hod ....

(H) *Complete these phrases by adding suitable words:—*
a .... of wolves.   a .... of ships.
a .... of bees.   a .... of singers.
a .... of whales.   a .... of thieves.
a .... of cattle.   a .... of savages.

EXERCISE 27

(A) *Select the correct word from the brackets:—*
A person who makes a speech is an (orator, artist, commentator).
A man who writes stories is an (artist, author, sculptor).
A bed on board ship is called a (bunk, cabin, saloon).
A vessel for holding flowers is a (caddy, scuttle, vase).
A surgeon operates in a (cinema, theatre, ward).

(B) *Choose the correct word from the brackets:—*
Sam as well as George (was, were) there.
Neither the one nor the other (were, was) right.
Fred is younger than (I, me).
I was sorry to part (of, with) that picture.
The book is different (to, from) the film.

(C) *Complete these phrases:—*
as blind as a ....   as pale as ....
as gentle as a ....   as good as ....
as dull as ....   as plain as a ....

(D) *Give the* OPPOSITES *of:—*
defend .... interior .... throw ....
broad .... innocent .... private ....

(E) *Supply* ONE *word for the phrases in italics:—*
Petrol, *which easily catches fire* is   ....
Smoking was *not allowed* in the garage. ....
The motorist drove *slowly and carefully.* ....
The boy *was very sorry for* his mean action............

37

(F) *Which words are* SIMILAR IN MEANING *to these?*
cease .... permit .... roam ....
external .... prompt .... imitate ....

(G) *What do we call the natives of these countries?*
Spain .... Sweden .... Holland ....
Turkey .... Finland .... Italy ....
Mexico .... Japan ....

(H) Complete these sentences:—
Food put on hooks to lure fish is called ....
The opposite of "increase" is ....
When animals go to sleep in winter
    they are said to................................
A person who eats no meat is called a ....
Savages who eat human flesh are called ....
P O — — A — L E means "easily carried about."

EXERCISE 28

(A) *Give words* SIMILAR *in meaning to*:—
vacant .... aid .... amount ....
protect .... commence ..... repair ....

(B) *Supply* ONE *word in place of the phrases in italics*:—
The runner was *completely tired and worn out.*

$\qquad\qquad\qquad\qquad$ EX ....

The rude girl *broke into* the conversation.

$\qquad\qquad\qquad\qquad$ INT ....

He *changed his appearance by dressing* himself as a
policeman. $\qquad$ DIS ....

(C) *Insert the* ONE *apostrophe in* EACH *sentence*:—
I forgot to take Toms book to the library.
The childrens clothes were lost.
All the girls hats were sent to Mrs. Smith.
Some of the pianos strings were broken.

(D) *Insert the capital letters and punctuate this sentence*:—
this will warm you said mother as she served the soup

(E) *Write down the* VERBS *in these sentences*:—
The great liner sailed slowly.
Merrily chimed the Christmas bells.
Stand here, Mary.
John has forgotten his satchel.

(F) *Complete these sentences by using a word formed from the word in brackets*:—
The joy .... news spread rapidly. (joy).
The singer sang beaut.... at the concert. (beauty).
I tried to pleas .... the child. (pleasant).
It was decided to dee........ the river. (deep).
He was a pupil of outstanding ab...... (able).

(G) *Complete these* PROVERBS:—
Make hay while ....
People who live in glass houses ....
An apple a day ....
Necessity is the ....

(H) WHOM *do you associate with*:—
a saw?...............   a pulpit? ....
a joystick? ....   a ship? ....
spectacles?............   a baton? ....
an anvil? ....   a palette? ....
a prescription? ....   a safety lamp ? ....

EXERCISE 29

(A) *Give* ONE *word answers for*:—
A machine that plays records.   ....
A place where aeroplanes land and take off............
An instrument that measures cold and heat............
A stream that flows into a river.   ....
A man who repairs frozen water pipes.   ....
The people who decide whether a prisoner
  is guilty or not.   ....
A floating mass of ice.   ....

(B) *Complete these* PROVERBS:—
A stitch in time ....
It's no use crying over ....
Set a thief to ....
It never rains but ....

(C) *Using the words in capitals, make* ADJECTIVES *so as to complete these sentences*:—
BEAUTY. The lady wore a b .... dress.
EXPENSE. The car was an ex .... one.
GLORY. It was a gl .... victory.
SHAME. To steal is a sh .... deed.

(D) *Select the correct word from the brackets*:—
Many fruit trees grew in the (menagerie, orchard, garage).
We were amused by the kitten's (stupidity, antics, insolence).
Only vain people pay attention to (quality, duty, flattery).
To ensure success, you must be (impertinent, feeble, diligent).
His red uniform made him (audible, legible, conspicuous).

(E) *Give the* OPPOSITES *of these words*:—
ancestor ....   arrival ....
punishment ....   fortune ....
arrest ....   moving ....

(F) *Write down the* PLURALS *of these words*:—
cupful .... cloth .... bush ....
by-way .... buffalo .... bus ....
hanger-on ..... vase ....

(G) *Complete this table*:—

I run	I ran	I have run
I am	....	....
I hurt	....	....
I eat	....	....
I sing	....	....

(H) *Supply the* FEMININES *of these words*:—

master ....   tiger ....

monk ....   stallion ....

son-in-law ....   author ....

widower ....   emperor ....

EXERCISE 30

(A) *Correct the following sentences*:—

Everyone in the crowd were pleased with the score.

She has to lay down for an hour every afternoon.

He will do it easy, even if you cannot.

To who did you give the book?

(B) *Write down the* OPPOSITES *of*:—

hate .... more .... obedient ....

innocent .... pure .... normal ....

(C) *Read this example and then complete the following*:—

    e.g. Something amusing gives   Amusement.

A strong man has   S ....

An angry lion shows   A ....

To explain means to give an   E ....

To conclude means to come to a   C ....

A wise person shows   W ....

(D) *What name is given to a person who*:—

extracts teeth?   ....

solves murders?   ....

prescribes medicine?   ....

makes and repairs shoes?   ....

writes for newspapers and magazines?   ....

(E) *From the words in capitals, make suitable* NOUNS *to complete these sentences*:—

INVITE.   I received an IN .... to the party.

ABLE.   He showed great AB .... as a cricketer.

PURE.   The P .... of the water was well known in the district.

(F) *Insert the capital letters and punctuate the following*:—

i took my brothers skates into manchester so that mr robinson could repair them.

41

(G) *Complete these phrases with appropriate words*:—
the .... of a hinge.　the .... of a horn.
the .... of brakes.　the .... of coins.
the pealing of ....　the call of a ....

(H) *Write down the* TWO *words related to the one given*:—
Clock.　(hands, wristlet, face, shovel, cushion).
Sun.　(rays, harbour, sermon, heat, crescent).
Rifle.　(barrel, trigger, candle, mirror, arrow).
Pipe.　(towel, packet, stem, bowl).

(I) *Complete these phrases*:—
a bird's eye ....　a cat on ....
a stiff upper ....　a storm in a ....
a fly in the ....　by hook or by ....

EXERCISE 31

(A) *Complete these phrases with appropriate words*:—
the .... of silk.　the .... of water.
the slam of a ....　as cunning as a ......
the popping of ....　as .... as a mule.

(B) *In what containers or buildings are the following kept?*
tea ....　coal ....　swords ....
flowers ....　clothes ....　gas ....
pistols ....　locomotives ....　books ....

(C) *Give* ONE *word for the phrase in italics*:—
This place looks *as if I had seen it before.* f..........
He lived in the *very top room of the house.* a..........
Writing papers, pens, etc., sold here.　s..........

(D) *Complete these phrases*:—
a suite of ....　as .... as an eel.
a .... of trees.　as heavy as ....
as flat as a ....　as purple as the ....

42

(E) *By choice from the brackets, indicate what these expressions mean:—*

"A CHIP OF THE OLD BLOCK" means (very like father, a piece of wood, a wound in the head).

"AT LOGGERHEADS" means (with lumberjacks, quarrelling, pleased with something).

"AN OLD SALT" means (a packet of salt, a strong man, an experienced sailor).

"TO SMELL A RAT" means (to be wrong, be suspicious, to catch mice).

"SON OF A GUN" means (pistol, likeable rascal, blacksmith).

(F) *Complete these sentences with suitable* PAIRS *of words:—*

After the dangers of the journey they were glad to be home s . . . . and s . . . .

The police strive to maintain l . . . . and o . . . .

John looked s . . . . and s . . . . in his uniform.

I keep o . . . . and e . . . . in that box.

(G) *Arrange each group of words in alphabetical order:—*

gather   gain   gait   garden   gas

. . . .

brood   banter   bait   bell   best

. . . .

shadow   shack   shovel   slack   shilling

. . . .

EXERCISE 32

(A) *Choose the correct word from those given and fill in the blanks:—*

refrigerator, ventilated, pasteurised, hygienic.

I insist on having my room well . . . .

Put the food in the . . . . and keep it fresh.

Milk is . . . . to free it from germs.

. . . . habits safeguard health.

(B) *Insert the capital letters and punctuate this sentence:—*

i let him in said james and he has been here for some time.

(C) *Use* ONE *word to describe* EACH SET *of words*:—
pliers, spanners, hammers, saws. ....
gold, lead, silver, iron. ....
measles, scarlet fever, mumps, diphtheria............
motor car, bus, lorry, van. ....
sword, rifle, cutlass, revolver. ....

(D) *Use* ONE *word in place of the words in italics*:—
Phil *kept out of the way of* Mrs. Stewart.............
The vase was broken *quite by accident.* ....
During the *great shortage of rain* the crops............
died.
That poor person is *out of his mind.* ....
I think your work is getting better and............
better.

(E) Indicate, by a sentence, the meaning of these expressions:—
"TO KICK UP A DUST" means (to spring clean, to jump
about, to make a disturbance about something).
"TO PLAY THE GAME" means (play music, behave fairly, to
take part in a contest).
"TO BURY THE HATCHET" means (dig up the garden, to
make peace with someone, chop firewood).

(F) *Complete these sentences with suitable words*:—
The old colonel was purple with ....
The bully turned white with ....
The little orphan was blue with ....
His rival was green with ....
The pages of the book were yellow with ....

(G) *Supply the missing words*:—
I .... means "cannot be seen."
One hundred years is called a ....
The meat of a cow is called ....
"Many hands make ...."

EXERCISE 33

(A) *Correct the following sentences:*—
Between you and I, I think the film was disappointing.
The twins sung very well.
He jumped off of the bus.
Jim didn't know what he was doing of.
Neither of them are tall.

(B) *What do we mean by these popular phrases?*
"Good for nothing." ....
"Hard up." ....
"Out of sorts." ....
"Minding one's p's and q's." ....

(C) *Words are often grouped into pairs by using the conjunction "and". Here are some mixed words which you must place into their correct pairs:*—
white crop head neck black shoulders easy free
....

(D) *Complete these sentences by forming* NOUNS *from the adjectives in capitals:*—
OBEDIENT. The dog was famed for its o ....
PLEASING. It was a p .... to go to his house.
BRAVE.   The soldier was rewarded for his b........
WISE.   We find w........ usually in older people.

(E) *What do these abbreviations mean?*
M.P. ....   H.R.H. ....
Dr. ....   etc. ....

(F) *Select the* ONE *word which is different from the rest in the group:*—
Page, line, chapter, paragraph, paper.
Bicycle, car, pedestrian, lorry.
Plum, orange, bread, cherry.
Dog, cat, lion, canary, leopard.

(G) *Indicate, by a sentence, the meanings of these expressions:—*
"TO DRAW THE LONG BOW" means (to take aim, to tell incredible stories, to draw a picture).
"TO HAVE A FEATHER IN ONE'S CAP" means (to look nice, to be stupid, to have something to be proud of).
"TO THROW UP THE SPONGE" means (to give up, play in the bath, to challenge someone).

(H) *Complete these expressions:—*

as stiff as a . . . .   as right as . . . .
as dead as a . . . .   as clear as . . . .
as slow as a . . . .   a . . . . of puppies.

EXERCISE 34

(A) *Complete these sentences by forming* NOUNS *from the words in capitals:—*
DESCRIBE. The d . . . . of the lost boy was given to to the police.
FAMOUS. The runner's f . . . . soon spread throughout the school.
HIGH. The boy climbed to a great h . . . .
CURIOUS. Our c . . . . . . can often lead us into trouble.
SELECT. The s . . . . of the team is made every Thursday.

(B) *Write down the* OPPOSITES *of these words:—*
external . . . . sane . . . . defend . . . .
legal . . . . aware . . . . worse . . . .

(C) *By writing a sentence, indicate the correct meanings of these sayings:—*
"LET SLEEPING DOGS LIE" means (don't stir up trouble, make a kennel for dogs, leave dogs well alone).
"TO SHOW A CLEAN PAIR OF HEELS" means (to keep oneself clean, jump up and down to keep warm, to escape by running).

"TO HIT BELOW THE BELT" means (a punch in the stomach, to act unfairly, to make trouble for someone).

(D) *Write* ONE *word in place of the words in italics*:—
The boy had always been *fair and truthful.* h............
Malcolm's handwriting was *easy to read.* l............
I was helped by *people living nearby.*   n............

(E) *Here are four abbreviated words. Write them out in full*:—

photo.............................
pram..............................
gym..............................
plane.............................

(F) *insert the capital letters and punctuate these two sentences*:—
the man shouted look out
....
where are you going this afternoon asked david
....

(G) *What would you expect to find in these containers?*
punnet .... envelope ...... till ....
keg .... scabbard ...... hold ....

(H) *What do these abbreviations mean?*
P.T.O. ....   G.P.O. ....
R.S.V.P. ....   P.C. ....
a.m. ....   p.m. ....

(I) *Complete this table*:—

I begin	I began	I have begun
I am	....	....
I break	....	....
I choose	....	....
I fly	....	....
I freeze	....	....

47

(J) *Insert these words into the sentences in their appropriate places*:—

suggested, replied, asked, shouted.

"Where are my books?" .... Billy.

"I do not know," .... his friend.

"Perhaps you left them in the classroom," ....
Tommy.

"They aren't there," .... Stephen from the next room, "because I had to tidy it up."

EXERCISE 35

(A) *Complete each sentence with words of* OPPOSITE MEANING *to those in italics*:—

The building was erected as a *temporary* construction and not as a .... one.

The policeman *arrested* the man, but he was soon ......

After so long in *captivity*, ... was very welcome.

(B) *Substitute single words of* SIMILAR MEANING *for the phrases in italics*:—

My brother visits me *every year*. ....

The moon *threw light* on the whole lake. ....

The doctor said the operation would be *free*............
from pain.

The teacher said, "*Look over* your work............
again."

When I pushed the wheel it *went round and*............
round.

The houses were *the same in all respects*. ....

(C) *What name is given to a person who*:—

plans buildings? ....

paints houses? ....

dispenses medicine? ....

amputates limbs? ....

takes part in a play? ....

drives a car for someone? ....

(D) *Correct the following sentences*:—
She drinks neither tea or coffee.
I cannot see it nowhere.
Their is a lot of lakes in Switzerland.
He can lift weights quite easy.
Near the old man is some wooden railings.
When we come into the room we seen two boys who was
    laughing.

(E) *Complete these phrases*:—
as bitter as .... as round as a ....
as strong as a .... as thick as ....
as bright as a .... as clean as a ....

(F) *Complete the sentences with appropriate words from the
    brackets*:—
There is the cat .... killed our (who, which, that).
    bird.
I shall not wait .... five (from, after, since).
    o'clock.
Where .... you yesterday,(are, were, went).
    Bob?
Between you and ...., I don't (I, me).
    believe it.
My brother is older than .... (me, I).

(G) *Insert the apostrophes in these sentences*:—
Many mens lives are happy.
The pups tails have been cut off.
Theyre not to be trusted, Im sorry to say.

(H) *Write down the* PLURALS *of these words*:—
ox .... cliff .... aquarium ....
chorus .... pansy .... man-servant .....
potato .... story .... man-of-war .....
                kiss ....

(I) *Complete the following sentences*:—
An instrument that magnifies small objects is a ....
An instrument that makes distant objects bigger is a
    ....

49

A .... allows people far apart to speak to each other.

A .... is an instrument that takes photographs.

A pair of .... are used for drawing circles.

(J) *Complete these sentences by choosing the most suitable of these words:*—

        wherein, where, whence, wherever, whereas

The ugly sisters asked Cinderella .... she had been.

The giant asked Jack .... he had come.

There was no ship .... he could be hidden.

.... we live, we must live honestly.

He thought his work was good, ... it was poor.

EXERCISE 36

(A) *Rewrite the following, separating the words and putting in capital letters and punctuation:*—

onedayiwaswalkingalongthelanetowardsthevillagesudde
nlyiheardthesoundofaracingcaristoppedwalkingandstood
bythehedgetoletthecarpassmesafelytomysurprisethedrive
rstoppedthecarjustafewfeetawayfromme

(B) *Complete these* PROVERBS:—

Where there's a will, ...

The least said ....

If you give him an inch ....

There's no smoke ....

(C) *Rewrite the following sentences correctly:*—

It seems that he has broke his leg.

His father learnt him French.

It is the best book of the two.

He told the dog to lay down.

They believed that us two had done it.

(D) *Substitute* ONE *word for each italicised phrase:*—

Five hundred soldiers were *taken prisoner*............

I *removed the wrapper from* the parcel. ....

The man *gave himself up* to the police. ....

50

(E) *Complete these phrases*:—

as keen as . . . .   the . . . . of water.
as quick as . . . .   the . . . . of chains.
as tough as . . . .   the . . . . of a door.
as flat as a . . . .   the . . . . of silk.

(F) *What is meant by the following abbreviations?*

M.P. . . . .   i.e. . . . .
e.g. . . . .   etc. . . . .
R.S.V.P. . . . .   B.Sc. . . . .

(G) *What do we call*:—

a man who makes public speeches?   . . . .
a man who finds out something new?   . . . .
a person who takes the place of another?   . . . .
a man who supplies spectacles?   . . . .

(H) *Write down the* OPPOSITES *of these words*:—

disappear . . . . . .   like . . . .   rapid . . . .
dark . . . .   sharp . . . .   sweet . . . .

(I) *Complete the sentences with suitable words*:—

This stream flows . . . . that lake.
William and James shared the fruit . . . . them.
The soldiers landed . . . . Glasgow.
The dog was attached . . . . the kennel . . . .
    a lead.

(J) *Complete these sentences by forming words from the words in capitals*:—

MARRIAGE. He was . . . . in England.
ACCIDENT. It was an . . . . action that caused the
        crash.
CIRCLE. A record is . . . . in shape.
PEACE. It is very . . . . in the countryside.
BURIAL. The man was . . . . under an avalance.

(K) *By completion, indicate the meaning of these well-known sayings*:—

"TO PULL SOMEONE'S LEG" means (to play a trick on
    someone; to pull off someone's boots; to behave
    unfairly).

"TO SIT ON THE FENCE" means (to look over the garden wall; not taking sides; daydreaming).

"TO HOLD ONE'S TONGUE" means (to keep silent about something; to hold your tongue when taking medicine; to make one look foolish).

EXERCISE 37

(A) *By completion, indicate the meaning of these well-known sayings*:—

"TO KICK UP A DUST" means (to jump about; to make a disturbance about something; to dust the house).

"NOT WORTH THE CANDLE" means (no need for a light; of little value; having no candles).

"TO PUT THE CART BEFORE THE HORSE" means (to start at the wrong end; to make a horse work harder; to make things easier).

(B) *Complete these phrases*:—

as slippery as an ......   as heavy as ....
as crafty as a ....   as large as ....
as light as a ....   as hungry as a ....

(C) *Complete these words using the clues given*:—

Cars, lorries, buses, etc.   V .... S.
To mind one's own   B .... S.
A list of priced goods, books, etc.,
                        C .... E.
A man who dispenses medicine from a prescription.
                        P H .... T.

(D) *Arrange these football teams in alphabetical order*:—
Montrose, Milwall, Manchester, Middlesborough, Mansfield.

(E) *Write down the* OPPOSITES *of these words by adding a* PREFIX:—

sincere ....   advantage ....
behave ....   connect ....
efficient ....   regular ....
selfish ....   intelligent ....

52

(F) *Correct the following sentences*:—
The boy and his sister has gone to Ireland.
I cannot wait no more.
Bob wrote so bad that I couldn't read it.
Everyone showed their pleasure by clapping.
He laid in bed until ten o'clock.

(G) *Write* ONE *word for each of these phrases*:—
Without waiting a minute—   i . . . .
Over and over again—   re . . . .
Those who were looking on—   s . . . .
Water which is neither hot nor cold— t . . . .
Someone from another country—   f . . . .

(H) *Insert the capital letters and punctuate this passage*:—
    i shant be long said donald well if you are late i will keep
your dinner hot for you his mother replied

(I) *From each clue write the* PROVERB *to which it refers*:—
It is dangerous to delay. . . . . (6 words).
A man who is once injured is careful to avoid danger in
    the future. . . . . (4 words).
Always do things while you can. . . . . (6 words).

(J) *Change* ALL *singulars into* PLURALS:—
I found the purse on my chair.
My ruler was smashed by the bully.
The echo could be heard over the valley.
My football boots are in my room at the end of the corridor.

(K) *Insert these words into the sentences in their appropriate
    places*:—
whispered, said, explained, muttered, pleaded.
The man . . . . that he would arrive at eight o'clock.
The boy . . . . to his teacher why he was late.
The bully . . . . under his breath.
He . . . . his secret in his mother's ear.
The criminal . . . . for his life.

EXERCISE 38

(A) *Choose that word from the brackets which has a* SIMILAR MEANING *to the word in capitals*:—
> HELP.   (kind, aim, aid, hopeless).
> OLD.   (new, century, ancient, modern).
> PLEASANT. (agreeable, suitable, pheasant).
> CAREFUL. (careless, carefree, cautious).

(B) *In these sentences, choose that word from the brackets which makes the sentence correct*:—
> Where have the boys put (there, their) football boots?
> I haven't (anything, nothing) to say.
> He (use, used) to be in the Navy.
> Jim drove the car as (slow, slowly) as possible.
> Jane sews better than (I, me).

(C) *From the brackets, choose the* OPPOSITE *of the word given and write it*:—
> PRETTY. (ugly, beautiful, fair).
> height. (length, weight, depth).
> BRIGHT. (dull, shining, clean).
> HOLLOW. (empty, solid vacant).

(D) *Change* ALL *singulars into* PLURALS:—
> The rabbit ran to its burrow.
> The boy kept a sharp knife in his pocket.
> My key was given to my manservant.

(E) *Choose the correct word from the brackets and complete the sentence*:—
> Bees are kept in an (aviary, apiary, aquarium).
> Films are shown in a (theatre, cinema, attic).
> An artist paints in a (studio, boardroom, wardroom).
> Someone who sells tobacco and cigarettes is a (newsagent, brewer, tobacconist).

(F) *Using the words in capitals, form words which make the actions occur in the* PAST:—
> e.g. DRINK.   I *drank* the cocoa while it was hot.
> SLAY.   St. George s............. the dragon.
> BEAR.   He b .... the pain in silence.

SPRING.	The cat s .... at the dog.
RISE.	The teacher r......... from his chair.
FLY.	The bird f......... very quickly to its nest.

(G) *Insert the capital letters and punctuate this sentence:—*
how many games have we this season asked donald as my father wants to know

(H) *Place the following phrases in the most suitable sentences:—*
ways and means,   ups and downs,   wear and tear, lock and key.
On catching the thief, the police placed him under
....
The teacher had to find .... of punishing the culprit.
In spite of ...., the car looked in good condition.
Most people have their ....

(I) *With which countries do you associate the following?—*

Uncle Sam.............	John Bull ....
Robert the Bruce	Mounties ....
a shamrock	a leek ....

(J) *Rewrite these sentences correctly:—*
This is the longest of the two pencils.
He said I spoke when I never said nothing.
On the mantelpiece is some ornaments.
They saw the boy who had fell in the water.
In the centre of the room was a little boy and girl.
A more luckier boy could not be found.

(K) *Complete these sentences with the appropriate prepositions:—*
I was conscious ...... somebody standing behind me.
Jane's hair was similar .... Susan's.
Long John Silver filled the barrel .... apples.
According .... the radio broadcast the weather is going to be colder.
The boy was guilty .... disobedience.

EXERCISE 39

(A) *Write the* FEMINIES *of these words*:—

baron .... sir ....
god .... bullock ....
marquis .... sire ....

(B) *Write these abbreviations in full*:—

R.I.P. .... H.M.S. ....
Co. .... P.S. ....
Sq. .... Terr. ....

(C) *Place the words in brackets in their appropriate positions in the sentences*:—

The .... girl admired the .... prince.
                                    (handsome, pretty).
The .... king laughed at the .... little
    girl.   (proud, vain).
The .... man was fond of .... furniture.
                                    (old, antique).
A .... woman should not eat .... meat.
                                    (fat, stout).

(D) *Complete these* PROVERBS:—

Many hands ....
All's well that ....
Better late ....
Discretion is the ....
Empty vessels ....

(E) *Write down the word from the brackets which has* a SIMILAR MEANING *to the word in capitals*:—

NOTICE.   (gaze, blind, seen, observe).
PECULIAR. (humorous, odd, familiar).
LEGEND.   (myth, tail, novel).
STUBBORN. (cruel, obstinate, strong).
RAVENOUS. (hungry, thirsty, stupid).

(F) *Answer these questions as simply as you can*:—

What do we call a man who protects sheep?
Which instrument tells us direction?
What is the name of the place where beer is made?

What is another name for "daybreak"?
What are the *five* human senses?
What do we call a sea creature with eight limbs?

(G) *From each set of words, find* TWO *words which* RHYME *with each other and write them down*:—
mine, agree, ogre, knee, kneel.
may, more, repay, repayment, hail.
wood, book, mould, cold, load.
rise, cows, snows, snowy, rose.
phrased, chased, best, list, haste.
beam, cream, plain, wait, beat.
table, audible, capable, edible, gable.
yacht, patch, rate, stitch, rot.

(H) *name both* PARENTS *of*:—

a cygnet	a duckling ....
a leveret .... ,.......	a foal ....
a gosling	a puppy ....

(I) *Complete these phrases*:—

as cunning as a	as thick as ....
as dead as a	as white as a ....
as dry as a	as soft as ....
as mad as a	as smooth as ....
as poor as a	as sober as a ....

(J) *Complete the following* COMPLEMENTS:—

doctor and patient	shopkeeper and ....
teacher and	employer and ....
king and	parent and ....
host and	speaker and ....
author and	leader and ....

(K) *Correct and rewrite these sentences*:—
"May I lend your pencil?" asked Timothy.
My father learnt me to swim very quickly.
"Who did you give my football to?" asked Mike.
It was him who came to clean the windows.
I didn't find nothing to make me think he didn't know what
he was doing of.

EXERCISE 40

(A) *Read the following passage carefully and then answer the questions* IN SENTENCE FORM:—

"The main runway lights suddenly came on as we made our final circuit before straightening out to land. A double line of yellow sodium lights led up to the runway and, as we came down the glide-path, we put on our powerful spotlights which flooded the surface of the runway so that we were able to land as easily as if it were still daylight."

From "I Fly the Atlantic," by V. E. MEARLES.

(1) What colour were the runway lights?
(2) What carried the powerful spotlights?
(3) On what did these spotlights shine?
(4) At what time of day does the action take place?
(5) What do you think would happen if no lights at all were used?

(B) *Correct and rewrite the following sentences*:—

He did not except the book.

She sent the invitation to you and I.

To who does this jacket belong?

The two boys divided the sweets among them.

A more kinder man never lived.

(C) *Supply the* OPPOSITES *of these words*:—

barren ....   retreat ....
condemn ....   majority ....
dull ....   never ....
grant ....   valuable ....

(D) *Indicate, by* A SENTENCE, *the correct meanings of these popular sayings*:—

"AT A LOOSE END" means (to have nothing to do; a loose knot; a tug of war).

"TO HIT THE NAIL ON THE HEAD" means (to hit a nail correctly; to be right; to knock someone's head to wake him up).

"HORSE PLAY" is (riding on a horse; hooliganism; the way horses behave towards one another).

(E) *Answer these questions by writing sentences*:—
Who is known as a "Jack Tar"?
Who is known as a "Tommy Atkins"?
What is a tripod?
What do we mean by "having a busman's holiday"?
What do we mean by saying "as the crow flies"?
What fact is common to a parable, a legend and a myth?

(F) *Insert the capital letters and punctuate this passage*:—
when i have found the key said jane i will put it back into
the cupboard where it belongs if you do find it said mr
robinson perhaps you will tell me immediately

(G) *Insert the apostrophes in the following sentences*:—
The ladies coats were placed in the cloakroom.
John took the childrens books to Mr. Jones.
In the corner of the room, we found some birds eggs.
Neither James nor Judys shoes were clean.
My schools desks are newer than those at my brothers.

(H) *Place these words in their alphabetical order*:—
acquaintance, absence, autumn, aeroplane

(I) *Complete these sentences with the appropriate
prepositions*:—
He complained .... a cold.
I disagreed .... my brother.
The poet was inspired .... the music.
The footballer protested .... the referee's decision.
He was regarded .... a fine actor.

(J) *Change these situations into* PLURALS:—
address ....   passer-by ....
belfry ....   chimney ....
hero ....   family ....

59

(K) *Fill each space correctly with one of these words*:—
rise, rose, raise, risen, raised.
The schoolboy .... his hat to the lady.
I .... this morning at seven o'clock.
I noticed the child .... from its chair.
My mother could not .... the lid of the scuttle.
By midday, the temperature had .... five degrees.

(L) *Write down the* QUESTIONS *for which the following are
answers*:—
"I am feeling very well, thank you."
"My books are in my desk."
"I was late because I had to go on an errand for my
mother."
"Our pencils were sharpened this morning."
"We took Tom to the hospital."

EXERCISE 41

(A) *Read the following passage carefully and then answer the
questions* IN SENTENCE FORM:—
   "As the sun set we crawled finally into our tent, put on all our warm
clothing and wriggled into our sleeping bags. We drank *vast*
quantities of liquid and had a satisfying meal out of our store of
delicacies: sardines on biscuits, tinned apricots, dates and biscuits,
and jam and honey. The tinned apricots were a great treat, but it was
necessary first to *thaw* them out of their frozen state over our roaring
stove. In spite of the great height, our breathing was almost *normal*
until a sudden exertion would cause us to pant a little."

From "The Ascent of Everest," by JOHN HUNT.

(1) When did the men wriggle into their sleeping bags?
(2) What did they eat with their biscuits?
(3) For what did they use the stove?
(4) What would make them pant?
(5) Why was it so cold?
(6) Give words *similar* in meaning to those in italics.
(7) What were the men doing to be at a great height?

(B) *Arrange these letters in alphabetical order*:—
g, x, a, f, m, s. ....
Re-arrange these words in DICTIONARY *order*:—
Greenland, Gibraltar, Guernsey, Germany.
....

(C) *Put each of these words*:—
swim, cry, roars, barks,
into its proper space:—
The dog ....
The lion ....
The fish ....
The babies ....

(D) *Supply the word which has a* SIMILAR MEANING *to the word in capitals*:—
WEALTHY. (poor, rich, unhappy).
ADORE. (hate, love, like).
DAMP. (wet, hot, dry).
PURSUE. (press, chase, play).

(E) *Write down the* PLURALS *of these words*:—
handkerchief ....   study ....
journey ....   gallery ....
museum ....   son-in-law ....
cargo ....   scissors ....

(F) *Complete the sentences with suitable prepositions*:—
He agreed .... me.
The child ran .... the house to see her mother.
She sang songs different .... mine.
I have a great dislike .... bullies.

(G) *Write down the* FEMININES *of these masculine words*:—
Negro ....   Billy-goat ....
bull ....   lad ....
colt ....   sir ....
nephew ....   widower ....
ram ....   stallion ....

(H) *Complete the following*:—

The rector, who lives in a r........., keeps his dog, Spot, in a k........ just outside the kitchen door. At the bottom of the garden, there is the bee h........... If we walk to the top of the hill, we can see some gipsies' c............... Farther along the lane are the army b....... which are always kept as clean as a .... by the soldiers who are as busy as ....

(I) *Complete these well-known sayings*:—

as .... as a bat.	as bold as ....
as ... as a March hare.	as gentle as a ....
as .... as an owl.	as frisky as a ....
as sober as a	as sound as a ....

(J) *State the* OPPOSITES *of these words*:—

often	late	possible ....
open	always	foreign ....
less	sufficient	

(K) *Where would you buy the following articles?*

fish	....
spectacles	....
paper, pens, pencils, etc.	....
meat	....
flowers	....
sweetmeats	....

(L) *Complete these "collections" with the most suitable words*:—

a .... of geese.	a pride of ....
a .... of corn.	a bouquet of ....
a .... of drawers.	a suite of ....
a galaxy of	a .... of singers.

(M) *Read this passage very carefully*:—

"Ben, the sheepdog, is out in all weathers. In winter, when the snow is on the ground, he has a very hard task. Sometimes sheep or lambs stray and are lost in the snow. Then Ben and his master must go and seek them out. Ben likes this game of hide-and-seek even though he is sometimes almost perished with cold. He is so pleased when he finds a lost lamb. He barks loudly and runs back to his master to tell him. The shepherd hurries to the spot where the lamb is lying. He picks up the lamb and shelters it in his arms."—*Original.*

Now answer these questions by writing sentence answers:—

(1) Who is Ben?..................
(2) How many different types of animals
    are mentioned? ....
(3) What name is given to a man who looks
    after sheep? ....
(4) What does Ben do when he finds a lost
    sheep? ....
(5) In which season of the year does Ben
    work very hard? ....
(6) Does Ben live in the town or country? ....

EXERCISE 42

(A) *Read the following passage carefully and then answer the questions in sentence form*:—

"I went on: night and darkness overtook me. No village was to be seen. The country was covered with snow and I was *unacquainted* with the road. Tired, I *alighted* and fastened my horse to something like a pointed stump of tree, which appeared above the snow. For the sake of safety, I placed my pistols under my arm and lay down on the snow, where I slept so soundly that I did not open my eyes till full *daylight*. It is not easy to conceive my *astonishment* at finding myself in the *midst* of a village, lying in a churchyard. Nor was my horse to be seen, but I heard him soon after neigh somewhere above me. On looking upwards, I *beheld* him hanging by his bridle to the weathercock of the steeple."

From "Baron Von Munchausen," by BRIAN ROBB.

(1) What did the apparent tree stump turn out to be?
(2) Did the traveller know where he was?
(3) Where did he place his pistols for safety?
(4) Where did he find himself in the morning?
(5) What word is used to express the sound a horse makes?
(6) Choose words similar in meaning, or more appropriate, to those in italics.

(B) *Express in a sentence the meaning of each of these sayings*:—

"TO TURN THE TABLES." . . . .

"TO LET THE CAT OUT OF THE
    BAG." . . . .

"TO HAUL OVER THE
    COALS." . . . .

(C) *Where would you look to find*:—

the names of the actors in a play? . . . .

the time of a train or bus? . . . .

the facts regarding the days of the year?. . . . .

a record of personal daily events? . . . .

a telephone number? . . . .

(D) *Complete this table*:—

e.g. big	bigger	biggest
old	. . . .	. . . .
bad	. . . .	. . . .
good	. . . .	. . . .
little	. . . .	. . . .
much	. . . .	. . . .

(E) *Here are some words known as "adverbs"*:—

heavily, furiously, silently, soundly, immediately,
    patiently.

Now place them in their appropriate spaces:—

He slept . . . .   He fell . . . .

He waited . . . .   He crept . . . .

He charged . . . .   He decided . . . .

(F) *Form* NOUNS *from the following words*:—

e.g. sad . . . . sadness.

thirsty	decide . . . .
angry	know . . . .
beautiful	practise . . . .
brave	gay . . . .

(G) *Write down the* PROVERBS *for which these questions are clues*:—

What must you not carry in one basket?

What isn't robbery?

When is there less speed?
How do we catch a thief?
Who catches the worm?

(H) *Write out these abbreviations in full:*—
C.O.D. ....   P.T.O. ....
i.e. ....   v. ....
J.P. ....   U.S.A. ....

(I) *Write down words* OPPOSITE *in meaning to those given:*—
maximum ....   generous ....
eminent ....   mountain ....
motorist ....   senior ....
plural ....   rural ....

(J) *Explain what is meant by these well-known expressions:*—
"BY HOOK OR BY CROOK" means ....
"A FLASH IN THE PAN" means ....
"TO TAKE FORTY WINKS" means ....

(K) *Re-arrange these jumbled letters so that they make words:*—
pihw ....   ctoar ....
ttehe ....   imgac ....
atirn ....   ooptat ....
ewiht ....   lcabk ....
laisro ....   yomra ....

(L) *Change each sentence from* DIRECT *to* INDIRECT *speech:*—
e.g. " I am going out," said Jim.—
Jim said that he was going out.

"Where are you going, Jane?" asked James.
"I shall not be long," called Stephen.
"I want two slices of steak delivered this afternoon," said Mrs. Jones.
"These chocolates are delicious," said Joan, "and we will buy some more."

EXERCISE 43

(A) *Read the following passage carefully and then answer the questions in sentence form*:—

"Sweet briar and southernwood, jasmine, pink, and rose, have long been yielding their evening sacrifice of incense: this new scent is neither of shrub nor flower; it is—I know it well—it is Mr. Rochester's cigar. I look round and I listen. I see trees *laden* with ripening fruit. I hear a nightingale warbling in a wood half a mile off; no moving form is *visible*, no coming step *audible*; but that *perfume* increases. I make for the wicket gate leading to the shrubbery, and I see Mr. Rochester entering. I step aside into the ivy recess; he will not stay long; he will soon return whence he came, and if I sit still he will never see me."

From "Jane Eyre," by CHARLOTTE BRONTE

(1) What made the new scent in the evening air?
(2) Which bird was singing in the wood?
(3) Does Jane Eyre hear or see Mr. Rochester coming?
(4) What does she do so that he does not see her?
(5) Choose words *similar in meaning* to those in italics.
(6) Would you say it was a warm or a cold evening?

(B) *Put these words into their appropriate places in the sentences*:—

lay, laid, lie.

I always .... on my back.
Tom .... the table for his mother yesterday.
He .... in bed until ten o'clock this morning.

(C) *Complete these sentences with words formed from those in capitals*:—

INVENT.　　His .... was concerned with television.
PRIDE.　　He was a very .... man.
OCCUPY.　　Susan's .... was that of private secretary.
MISCHIEF.　　Monkeys are ....
REASON.　　It is .... to expect people to wrap up in cold weather.

(D) *State the* TWO *words which* RHYME *in each group*:—
air, lean, heir, bread, here.

middle, meddle, waddle, medal, straddle.
chuck, cheque, chick, quack, check.
seal, scent, serial, cereal, peril.
paws, sows, pause, were, oar.

(E) *Write down the* YOUNG *of these animals*:—
wolf .... elephant .... goat ....
hare .... horse .... pig ....

(F) *Insert the capital letters and punctuate this passage*:—
    james said where are you going in this rain i shant be
very long jane replied i am just going to the stable to see if
the foal is all right

(G) *Complete these* PROVERBS:—
When the cat's away ....
Two heads are ....
Out of the frying pan ....
New brooms ....
Absence makes the heart ....

(H) *Place the following words in the sentences best suited to
their use*:—
closed, finished, stopped, completed, concluded, ended.
His watch .... at six o'clock.
I know how the story ....
I have .... my lessons.
The workmen have .... the alterations.
The meeting .... with the National Anthem.
Having enough money, they .... the fund.

(I) *Place* WHO, WHOM, WHOSE *in their correct positions in the
sentences*:—
That is the child .... found the purse.
That is the old man .... purse was stolen.
That is the boy .... I saw buying toffee.

(J) *Give words* SIMILAR IN MEANING *to the following*:—
excavate .... sufficient ....
comprehend .... vicinity ....
tranquil .... observe ....

67

(K) *Choose* TWO *of the four words in the brackets that are connected in some way with the word given*:—

TREE.   (wall, trunk, bough, lamp).
BICYCLE.   (pedals, hangar, bowl, pump).
TELEPHONE. (scabbard, receiver, needle, kiosk).
EYE.   (lashes, laughed, blinked, swinging).

(L) *Complete these phrases by adding suitable words*:—

the .... of feet.   a .... of horses.
the .... of hoofs.   a .... of clans.
the skirl of the ....   a .... of cards.
as changeable as the ...   a smuck of ....
as sick as a ....   a punnet of ....

(M) *Change each sentence from* INDIRECT *to* DIRECT *speech*:—

e.g. Jim said that he was going out—
"I am going out," said Jim.

Mrs. Smith said that she felt that children should go to bed early.

Bob asked Mr. Williams if he might borrow his ladder.

As he had an appointment with the dentist, Michael asked if he might leave early.

My mother told me to be careful when I crossed the road.

EXERCISE 44

(A) *Read the following passage carefully and then answer the questions in sentence form*:—

"The department at Scotland Yard which investigates or inquires into most of the more serious crimes is known as the Criminal Investigation Department—C.I.D. for short. It has hundreds of detectives whose work is to discover or detect who has committed crimes. Detectives do not wear uniforms even though they are only of the rank of detective constable. Criminals are always watching for policemen, and if they saw a constable in uniform they would be on their guard. Detectives therefore dress in plain clothes, and sometimes when they are on a special case they make themselves look like some other person. So that they will be able to prove they are members of the police force all detectives carry a card called a 'warrant card' which gives their name and rank."

From "The Arm of the Law," by G. A. CAMPBELL.

(1) How do detectives dress?
(2) Which words tell us that detectives often disguise themselves?
(3) What's a "warrant card"?
(4) Why don't detectives wear ordinary police uniform?
(5) Where is Scotland Yard?
(6) Write down these abbreviations in full:—

C.I.D.   P.C.   Sgt.

(B) *Complete these sentences with suitable prepositions*:—
I had to apologize .... the lady.
I was conscious .... a dog sniffing on the other side of the gate.
The man protested .... the policeman's action.
The fox had been the victim .... poisoning.
According .... my brother, it is cold enough for snow.
One need not be ashamed .... being poor.

(C) *Rewrite the following sentences correctly*:—
Neither of the singers were present.
She gave the apples to my sister and I.
Between you and I, I thought the film was very poor.
Either Timothy or Stephen have the book you wanted.
He is as tall as me.

(D) *Write another word which* SOUNDS *exactly the same as the words below although spelt differently*:—
fore .... knows .... maid ....
hair .... flour .... blew ....
hear .... fare .... cellar ....
quay ....

(E) *Complete the following with suitable words*:—
Picture is to .... as Carpet is to Floor.
.... is to Forest as Sheep is to Flock.
Hearing is to Ear as Sight is to ....
Wing is to Bird as Fin is to ....
.... is to Cygnet as Pig is to Piglet.

69

(F) *Complete these phrases by writing suitable "sound" words*:—

the .... of a drum.   the .... of silk.

the .... of water.   the .... of corks.

the .... of feet.   the .... of a hinge.

(G) *Opposite each animal write down the names given to the* MALE *and the* FEMALE:—

HORSE	....	....
PIG	....	....
RABBIT	....	....
SWAN	....	....
ELEPHANT	....	....

(H) *Write down words* SIMILAR IN MEANING *to*:—

commence ....   exterior ....

caution ....   assemble ....

dusk ....   transparent ....

quantity ....   rapid ....

remedy ....   gallantry ....

(I) *Give* ONE *word in place of those in italics in these sentences*:—

The prices were *made less than before*..............

The *people who were listening* applauded. ....

The germs in the air are *unable to be seen*............

His job is only *for the time being*. ....

The actor was *able to be heard* at the back of the hall. ....

(J) *Answer these questions*:—

O.H.M.S. is short for ....

The thistle is the national emblem of ....

What do we call a group of four musicians? ....

A sailor's map is known as a c — — — —.

What is a "gamp"? ....

What is meant by "scuttling" a ship? ....

What is the flesh of a deer called? ....

A centenarian is a person who is ....

Which letters do we call vowels? ....

The shallow crossing of a river is called a f — — —.

(K) *From the words in brackets choose the correct meaning of the word in capitals and thereby complete the sentences*:—

CONDIMENTS are   (seasonings, flattering remarks, underclothes).

A CONTROVERSY is a   (puzzle, dispute, greenhouse).

CONTRABAND is   (an orchestra, smuggled goods, a flower).

CONFIDENTIAL means (escorted, business-like, private).

CONCEIT means   (vanity, courtesy, modesty).

EXERCISE 45

(A) *Read the following passage carefully and then answer the questions in sentence form*:—

"On a late summer morning the ship ran into Dakar in a smooth sea which we knew was a veil of illusion *concealing* thousands of sharks. We had been preparing for Atlantic sharks for two years. We had the finest anti-shark *defence* ever devised by the mind of man and the stout blacksmiths of Toulon. It was an iron cage resembling a lion's in a sideshow; a collapsible structure which could be erected quickly and lowered into the water. It had a door through which a diver could go in and out under water and bar himself against sharks. We believed that sharks were most dangerous when a diver was entering or leaving the water. Now we could be lowered safely, *emerge* on the bottom for our work, return to the cell, lock ourselves in and be raised in complete *safety*. Inside the cage there was a buzzer for signalling the ship."

From "The Silent World," by J. Y. COUSTEAU.

(1) When were the sharks most dangerous to the divers?

(2) How could the divers signal to the ship if they were in danger?

(3) What did the divers intend to use to make them safe from sharks?

(4) In which ocean were the sharks?

(5) Who made the iron cage?

(6) Write down the OPPOSITES of the words in italics.

(B) *Insert the capital letters and punctuate this passage*:—

where are you going asked malcolm im off to the cinema replied Charles but i shall be home before you go round to mrs mackenzie

71

(C) *Give* ONE *word answers for:*—
a room used for physical training, ...
a bicycle made for two people, ...
a man who makes clothes, ...
the place where food is stored in a house, ...
the place where money is made, ...
wasps, ants, and bees, ...
when there is a scarcity of rain and water, ...
when there is a scarcity of food. . . . .

(D) *Write down the* OPPOSITES *of these words:*—
contract . . . . future . . . . dark . . . .
minimum . . . . . . generous . . . . legal . . . .
victory . . . . false . . . . obey . . . .
multiply . . . . approve . . . . juvenile . . . .

(E) *Complete the following* PROVERBS:—
A bad workman . . . .
It's a long lane that . . . .
One man's meat . . . .
More haste . . . .
Discretion is the better part . . . .

(F) *Put the apostrophes in their correct positions:*—
theyll, theyre, whereer, tis, neer, neednt.

(G) *Choose the correct word from the brackets and complete
the sentences:*—
The ship (sprang, sprung) a leak and (sank, sunk) within a
few minutes.
The boy has (ate, eaten) an apple and has (drunk, drank)
some milk.
John has (took, taken) his little brother home. He had
(tore, torn) his jacket.

(H) *Complete these sentences by the correct use of* TO *and*
TOO:—
It is . . . . soon . . . . say if they will live.
The boys tried . . . . swim . . . . far out to sea.
It is . . . . late now . . . . catch the train.
His head is . . . . big for his hat.

(I) *Write down words* SIMILAR IN MEANING *to the following*:—

instruct ....   occur ....

infirmary ....   disease ....

onlooker ....   miscellaneous ....

slay ....   peril ....

starvation ....   presently ....

(J) *Against each word write another word which* SOUNDS *exactly the same although spelt differently*:—

steal ....   boy ....

tail ....   meat ....

waist ....   mist ....

right ....   bare ....

none ....   gilt ....

(K) *Complete these phrases with suitable "sound" words*:—

the .... of the wind. the ..... of pens on paper.

the .... of a hen. the ..... of burning wood.

the .... of wings. the ...... of the bagpipes.

(L) *Choose the correct word from the brackets and complete the sentences*:—

I found him (lying, laying) on the bed.

Either you or your friend (are, is) to blame.

Our boys were better footballers than (them, they).

(Whom, Who) do you think I saw at the bus stop?

Each man (has, have) (his, their) own way of doing things.

EXERCISE 46

(A) *Read the following passage carefully and then answer the questions in sentence form*:—

"Early next morning we started off again. I filled a little Indian sack with all my precious notebooks containing perhaps 2,000 pages in which I had scribbled down the whole story of our expedition to date, and then I fastened the sack over my shoulder. Our canoes soon sped along in the centre of the current. It was no longer navigation in the ordinary sense; it was more like an obstacle race. We shot like toboggans down falls with an eight or nine feet drop. Each time the canoes filled with water almost to the gunwales, but their speed carried them on. And then we had to bale furiously in order to be ready for the next drop. In the afternoon my canoe completely disappeared in an enormous wave. The men saved the canoe and nearly all the cargo. All we lost this time was our collection of bows and arrows and one of our two guns. Unfortunately, my wounds opened up again, and the water around me was stained with blood. One of the men lifted me on his back and carried me to the shore."

From "The Impossible Adventure," by A. GHEERBRANT.

(1) What did the explorer use the Indian sack for?

(2) What did the explorer lose from his canoe when it capsized?

(3) How did he get to the shore?

(4) With what do we usually associate "toboggans"?

(5) Do you think the expedition was in a country of warm or cold climate?

(6) The word "bale" may be used in two ways.
    What do we mean when we say:—
    "to bale out of an aeroplane"? ....
    "to bale out of a boat"? ....

(B) *Complete these sentences by using the words* THERE, THEY'RE *and* THEIR.

.... is no doubt that they will bring ....
raincoats.

If .... is no match, ... money will be
refunded.

" .... coming to tea," said Mother.

.... was a lot of trouble when the builders arrived
because they didn't bring .... proper tools.

74

(C) *Select the correct word from the brackets*:—

My brother and (I, me) waited in the bus queue, for mother
had given (he, him) and (I, me) the fare.

The man to (who, whom) I had given the book was the one
(who, whom) followed me home this evening.

(D) *Rewrite the following sentences using* ONE *word only in
place of the words in italics*:—

When the bell sounded, the children left *in a hurry*.

The actor acted *with great skill*.

We decided to make camp before *the sun had set*.

The wolf *ate up greedily* the meat I threw to him.

We all knew that he was a *person who spent wastefully*.

(E) *Insert the capital letters and punctuate these sentences*:—

yes sir i have finished it said james proudly

can i help you robert asked mr jenkins

can you bring a torch asked dick

as i am going out said mary i will get your shopping

jane said quietly i dont think i am very well

(F) *Complete these phrases*:—

as green as . . . .   a leap of . . . .
as regular as the . . . .   a . . . . of cards.
as smooth as . . . .   a . . . . of trees.
as . . . . as leather.   a truss of . . . .
as . . . . as a monkey.   a . . . . of magistrates.

(G) *Correct and rewrite the following sentences*:—

Neither Jim or Robert is right.

His hair needs cutting badly.

The man came in the room and said, "You done it."

Between you and I, I think your ticket is different to mine.

To who does this book belong?

The goalkeeper was the tallest of the two boys.

(H) *Write down the* PLURALS *of these singulars*:—

quantity . . . .   passer-by . . . . . .   luxury . . . .
volcano . . . .   housewife . . . . . .   bye-law . . . .
batsman . . . .   dress . . . .

75

(I)   *Complete these sentences with words formed from those in capitals*:—

CRITIC.   It is easy to c . . . . other people.

INFORM.   A railway timetable gives us i . . . . about trains.

EXPENSE.   I had an e . . . . present for Christmas.

MYSTERY.   The manner in which the horse disappeared was very m . . . .

SOLUTION.   The detectives were able to s . . . . the crime.

(J)   *Supply words* SIMILAR IN MEANING *to the following*:—

collision	fault	robust . . . .
enough	flavour	convenient . . . . . .
fable	apparel	common . . . .
	loathe	

(K)   *Give both* PARENTS *of these young animals and people*:—

prince	. . . .	. . . .
lamb	. . . .	. . . .
child	. . . .	. . . .
foal	. . . .	. . . .
nephew	. . . .	. . . .
chicken	. . . .	. . . .

EXERCISE 47

(A)   *Read the following passage carefully and then answer the questions in sentences*:—

"The *midday* sun beat down unmercifully on to the cobbled street. Janet, who was dressed in a light frock and sandals, walked leisurely but firmly along the road towards the park. She had little thought for the people she passed, for her expectations lay in the direction of the bagpipes, whose unique music was drifting towards her from the park. She was visualizing her father and brother gaily dressed in their kilts and anxious for the Games to *commence,* whilst her mother would already be waiting *impatiently* for the picnic tea. As she approached the park, Janet's pace clearly *quickened* and the impulse to run was checked only by the *heat* of the sun."—*Original.*

(1) In which country do you think the action takes place?

(2) Write down the correct meaning of "visualizing" from the following:—

to see a ghost; a view through rows of trees; to picture in the mind; to go to see.

(3) Write down the correct meaning of the word "unique" from the following:—

(peculiar; disagreeable; loud; unlike anything else).

(4) Why was Janet lightly dressed?

(5) State the OPPOSITES of the words in italics in the passage.

(B) *Complete these sentences with the correct words taken from the brackets*:—

I will wait . . . . you at the station.   (for, on).

Joan had . . . . the letter very well.   (written, wrote).

None of us . . . . able to play the game.   (is, are).

He has . . . . to the cinema.   (went, go, gone).

John and his brother . . . . good friends.   (was, were).

(C) *State the* ONE *word which does not fit in with the rest of each group*:—

Cat, dog, potatoes, pig.

Chair, cupboard, table, ceiling.

Red, blue, white, apple.

Gramme, millimetre, centimetre, metre, kilometre.

Mother, father, cousin, uncle, girl.

(D) *Insert the capital letters where necessary*:—

we all went to manchester last august.

last saturday, i went to visit mrs. grundy.

(E) *Re-arrange these words so as to make sentences*:—

to-morrow are going picnic a we for

well I feeling am very not

win match we yesterday did football not the

(F) *Change these singulars into* PLURALS:—

axe .... Eskimo .... torpedo ....
canary .... deer .... maid-of-honour.....
woman .... outlaw .... cherry ....
guinea ....

(G) *Write down the* FEMININES *of*:—

king   bachelor   father   lion   bull

Write down the MASCULINES *of*:—

girl   goose   wife   actress   duck

(H) *Complete the following phrases*:—

a gust of ....   as proud as a ....
a .... of rascals.   as .... as Job.
a clutch of ....   as keen as ....
a hand of ....   as deaf as a ....
a .... of grapes.   as playful as a ....

(I) *Complete these sets of adjectives. The first one has been completed*:—

tall,   taller,   tallest   little, ..., ...
good, ..., ...   bad, ..., ...
early, ..., ...   beautiful, ..., ...

(J) *We say a boy is "popular" if he is liked by everyone. Which word would you use to describe*:—

A boy who is always on time? A .... boy.
A dog which does what it is told? An .... dog.
A man who looks on the bright side of things? An .....
     man.
An author who is well-known? A .... author.
A castle which is very old? An .... castle.
A man who looks on the gloomy side of things? A .....
     man.

(K) *Choose that word from the brackets which means nearly the* SAME *as the word in capitals*:—

HIDEOUS.   (hidden, dreadful, pretty, young).
CONCEITED.   (vain, pleasant, handsome).
SITE.   (platform, path, place).
BRIEF.   (long, funny, short, broad).
FATIGUE.   (weariness, plump, insolent, bright).

(L) *What do we mean when we use these expressions?*—
"TO BE IN THE SAME BOAT." . . . .
"TO BE DOWN IN THE
    MOUTH."   . . . .
"TO BE OUT OF SORTS."   . . . .
"TO MAKE NO BONES ABOUT
    SOMETHING."   . . . .

(M) *Complete these* PROVERBS:—
Cut your coat according to . . . .
It's an ill wind that blows . . . .
Little boys should be seen . . . .
One swallow does not . . . .

(N) *Complete the following table*:—

I break	I broke	I have broken
I awake	. . . .	. . . .
I bring	. . . .	. . . .
I draw	. . . .	. . . .
I drive	. . . .	. . . .
I shake	. . . .	. . . .

EXERCISE 48

(A) *Read the following passage carefully and then answer the questions by writing sentences*:—
"Christopher Columbus was born in 1450 in the city of Genoa in Italy, the son of a Genoese weaver. As a boy he used to listen to the wonderful stories of Marco Polo and to the exciting tales of the sailors in Genoa. When he grew up, he became a sailor and did much sailing in the Mediterranean and off the coast of Portugal. At this time, people were saying that the world was round and not flat. This made Columbus wonder whether he could find a way to India and China by sailing across the Atlantic Ocean. Nobody knew at that time what was on the other side of the Atlantic. People thought his idea was ridiculous and they laughed at him. The kings of England, France and Portugal would not help him. After many years of waiting, Queen Isabella of Spain gave him three little ships, the *Santa Maria,* the *Pinta* and the *Nina.* Seamen were afraid to join Columbus' ships and he had to be content with men from the prisons. He set sail from Palos in August, 1492.
"After many weeks of fear, hardship and near mutinies, Columbus sighted land in November. He rowed ashore and set up the Spanish

flag on the land which he believed to be India. In fact he had discovered a new world—later to be called the West Indies. He sailed round some of the islands, namely Watling Island, Haiti and the Bahamas, before returning home. A year later, Columbus made another voyage, this time finding Jamaica. A third voyage took him to Trinidad, and the fourth voyage to the mainland of Central America—to Nicaragua and Panama. These were in 1498 and 1502. He was treated shamefully by the people who settled in the West Indies and he received no reward at all for his great discoveries. In 1504, he died a very poor man."— *Original.*

(1) Was Columbus an Italian or a Spaniard?

(2) How long did it take him to cross the Atlantic Ocean?

(3) What was his object in crossing the Atlantic Ocean?

(4) Who helped Columbus to set sail, and what was he given?

(5) How many voyages to the West Indies did Columbus make?

(6) How old was he when he died?

(7) From where did Columbus obtain his seamen?

(8) Do you think people appreciated his great discovery?

(B) *Write down that word from the brackets which has* A SIMILAR MEANING *to the word in capitals*:—

RAIMENT.   (clothing, anger, reward).

ORIGIN.   (present, beginning, meaning).

RENOWN.   (fame, unknown, popularity).

INTERNAL.   (exterior, difficult, inside).

INHABIT.   (dwell, forgive, prohibit).

SUFFICIENT. (abundance, scarcity, enough).

(C) *Write down the* HOMES *of these people and creatures*:—

parson	cow ....
Red Indian	eagle ....
tinker	pigeon ....
king	snail ....
Eskimo	badger ....

(D) *Insert the capital letters and punctuate these sentences*:—
fred asked can anyone tell me what happened
oh screamed mary the house is on fire

80

Now insert the full-stops, capital letters and commas in this passage:—

then with relief i remembered i had my pistol tucked away in my hip pocket i whipped it out i was expecting one or other of them to rush at me but with my back to the wall and pistol in hand i began to feel safe.

(E) *Complete these phrases*:—

a ray of .... a crumb of ....

a breath of .... a speck of ....

a gust of .... a pinch of ....

a wisp of .... a pat of ....

(F) *Choose the correct meaning of each saying*:—

"EVERY DOG HAS IT'S DAY" means (every one has his turn; a dog's birthday; dogs enjoy the daytime).

"TO FACE THE MUSIC" means (to watch the band; to face up to your troubles; to read music).

"TO MAKE A CLEAN BREAST OF IT" means (to confess to something; to scrub one's chest; to break a friendship).

(G) *For each phrase write* ONE *appropriate word*:—

 (i) go back   = to ....

 (ii) go down   = to ....

(iii) go into   = to ....

(iv) go forward = to ....

 (v) go up   = to ....

(vi) go on hands and knees = to.....................

(H) *Choose the correct word from each bracket*:—

I spoke to (he, him) and (she, her).

(Who, Whom) are (they, them)?

I think he is as tall as (I, we) but his brother is the (tallest, taller).

Repeat the (two last, last two) lines of the song.

The money was divided between my sister and (I, me).

(I) *Rewrite each sentence in the* PAST TENSE:—

e.g. I drink tea but also like lemonade.

I *drank* tea but also *liked* lemonade.

He tells me that I write very well.

My brother and I fight like tigers, but we are good friends.

The wind blows and I become so cold that I cannot feel my
fingers.

(J) *Complete the following table*:—

Adjective	Noun	Verb
long	length	lengthen
sad	....	....
attractive	....	....
wide	....	....
beautiful	....	....
strong	....	....
satisfactory	....	....

(K) *Write out these abbreviations in full*:—

E.E.C. .... viz. .... R.A.F. ....
J.P. .... R.N. .... U.N.O. ....

(L) *Complete the following* PROVERBS:—

Absence makes the ....

Charity begins ....

He laughs best who ....

The early bird ....

Two heads are ....

(M) *Complete this table as the example shows*:—

	Similar	Opposite
REPAIR	MEND	DAMAGE
REVEAL	....	....
EXTERNAL	....	....
INDUSTRIOUS	....	....
COLLECT	....	....
BRAVE	....	....

(N) *Select the correct word or words from each bracket*:—

James was honest and (deceptive, diligent).

The (remedy, illness) or cure is a simple one.

The man was careful (because, lest) he should fall.

To show the white feather means (to capture a Red Indian,
to be cowardly).

The girl wept (faintly, bitterly).

He suffers (from, of) a swollen head.

My brother complained (with, of) of a headache.

A stream flowing into a river is called a (brook, tributary, rivulet).

The prisoner was not (allowed, aloud) his freedom.

His friend and (he, him) travelled to London.

(O) *Starting with the* SMALLEST, *grade each group of words as shown in the example:—*

    e.g. centimetre, kilometre, metre, millimetre.

    millimetre, centimetre, metre, kilometre.

mansion, hut, bungalow, cottage, palace.

. . . .

city, country, town, continent, village.

. . . .

punched, touched, battered, tapped, knocked.

. . . .

kettle, cup, pail, teapot, tub.

. . . .

fingered, slapped, patted, caressed.

. . . .

(P) *With whom do you associate the following?—*

putty	a truncheon . . . .
an anvil	a stethoscope . . . .
mail	a wig . . . .
handcuffs	bait . . . .
a canvas	contraband . . . .

EXERCISE 49(A)

(A) *Choose the correct word from the brackets:—*

(Was, Were) they not pleased to find that we (were, was) joking?

Anybody (are, is) allowed to travel on a bus.

None of the boys (have, has) seen the fireworks.

Either Jim or Jane (has, have) made the mistake.

All but Nora (has, have) been to my house for tea.

Mary is bigger than (me, I) but her little sisters are younger than (us, we).

(B) *Write down the* PLURALS *of these singulars*:—
tornado .... sheaf .... foundry ....
remedy .... oasis .... necessity ....
dwarf .... goose ....

(C) *Correct the following sentences*:—
I cannot run no farther.
Of the two, I like James best.
The man learnt me to swim very quick.
A man and his dog was at the corner of the street.
Neither of them have been very fortunate.

(D) *Which of the following words would appear last in a dictionary?*:—
scarf, seen, scent, septic, scene, satin.
Which of the following words would appear first?—
revolution, rover, revoke, reward, reynard, revolt.

(E) *Write down the* OPPOSITES *of these words*:—
compulsory .... secure .... rare ....
audible .... more .... honest ....
land .... shallow .... everywhere .....
nothing ....

(F) *Animals make different sounds. For example, we say a dog "barks". Give descriptive words for the sounds of these creatures*:—
a donkey ...... a lion .... a monkey ....
an elephant .... a pig .... a bull ....
a horse .... a crow ....

(G) *What do we call the* HOMES *of these animals and people?*
vicar .... horse .... hare ....
fox .... minister .... squirrel ....

(H) *The first pair in each question show you what to do. Complete the second pair.*
e.g. drink, drank; fly, f l e w
good, better;   bad   — — — — —
ancient, old;   purchase   — — —
sole, soul;   one   — — —
have, had;   am   — — —

84

(I) *Write down the* FEMININES *of these masculines*:—

Jew ....   colt ....
manager ....   fox ....
stepfather ....   nephew ....
ram ....   tom-cat ....

(J) *Answer these questions about* PROVERBS:—

What is a miss as good as? ....
What do birds of a feather do? ....
When should you make hay? ....
What does every cloud have? ....
What do empty vessels make? ....

(K) *Write down words* SIMILAR IN MEANING *to the following*:—

renown ....   proprietor ....
vacant ....   conversation ....
conclude ....   conceal ....
munch ....   feeble ....
perpendicular ....   ovation ....

(L) *Complete these phrases*:—

as bold as ....   a .... of whales.
as obstinate as a ....   a .... of furniture.
as large as ....   a .... of ships.
as brown as a ....   a skein of ....
as sour as ....   the rustle of ....
as true as ....   a regiment of ....

(M) *Rewrite each of the following after selecting* TWO *words, one in each pair of brackets*:—

    e.g. Kitten is to Cat as (calf, *puppy,* lamb) is to (horse, lion, *dog*).

    Happy is to Sad as (comedy, history, novel) is to (adventure, tales, tragedy).

    Film is to Cinema as (play, programme, director) is to (star, theatre, stage).

    Tadpole is to (bush, frog, duckling) as Caterpillar is to (butterfly, pond, insect).

(N) *Read these words*:—

but he missed one thing he longed to see a human face and hear a human voice at last he could bear the lonely life no longer he left the cave

After which word would you put the *first* full-stop?

. . . .

After which word would you put the *second* full-stop?

. . . .

How many sentences are there altogether?

. . . .

Now insert the capital letters and punctuate these two sentences:—

(a) the man turned the corner of montague road and walked towards mr duncans house

(b) dont forget to bring your football boots tomorrow said jim hawkins because we are playing against blackwell school

(O) *Complete these sentences with words formed from those in capitals*:—

SATISFY.   Some men obtain much S - - - - - - - - - - - from smoking.

ACCURATE.   The cricketer was famous for the A - - - - - - - of his bowling.

OCCASION.   We go to the pictures only O - - - - - - - - - - - -.

SHARP.   Last night, I S - - - - - - - - my saw with a file.

THINK.   I do not like the T - - - - - - of going to the dentist.

(P) *Write out in full the meanings of these abbreviations*:—

e.g. . . . . a.m. . . . . P.T.O. . . . .
C.O.D. . . . . i.e. . . . . B.C. . . . .

(Q) *Complete the meanings of these popular sayings*:—

"AT LOGGERHEADS WITH SOMEONE" means (to cut down trees with someone; to be suspicious of someone; quarrelling with someone).

"TO THROW UP THE SPONGE" means (to give up; to meet the worst; to get into trouble).

86

"TO BLOW ONE'S TRUMPET" means (to play in a band; to boast about something; to argue).

"TO STRIKE WHILE THE IRON IS HOT" means (to act without delay; to anger; to keep going).

(R) *Substitute that word from the brackets which is* SIMILAR IN MEANING *to the word in capitals*:—

The secretary was CAPABLE. (charming, busy, competent, energetic).

It was necesssary to ABANDON the game. (forsake, postpone, cancel).

The glass was very BRITTLE. (pretty, fragile, lovely).

(S) *Read the following*:—

> "I dance on your paper,
> I hide in your pen,
> I make in your ink-stand
> My little black den;
> And when you're not looking
> I hop on your nose,
> And leave on your forehead
> The marks of my toes."

From "The Education of Uncle Paul" by ALGERNON BLACKWOOD.

Now choose the most suitable title for this verse:—

> "The Money Spider."
> "Jack o' the Inkpot."
> "The Dancing Fly."

EXERCISE 49(B)

Read the following extracts and answer the questions beneath them by writing sentences:—

(A)

"It was late when Jane reached home. She knew that her mother would be out so she went to the back gate because a spare key had been put in the shed. She searched for the key but could not find it. Then she heard footsteps near the gate and was delighted to see her brother James standing there.

"She told him that she could not find the key and asked him what they should do. James thought for a moment and then remembered that his bedroom window was open. He gripped the drainpipe and began to climb up towards the window. Soon he had reached it and put out his leg towards the sill. Jane heard a cry of pain as James slipped and scratched his legs against the rough wall."—*Original.*

(1) Where was the spare key put? . . . .
(2) Whose footsteps did Jane hear? . . . .
(3) Whose bedroom window was
    open? . . . .
(4) What scratched James' legs? . . . .
(5) Did James fall to the ground? . . . .

(B)

"Dr. Rhodes made arrangements for the making of the shell. He first got the use of the largest gun in America. He had a shell made to fit this gun and the shell was made exactly to the scientist's plan. The trial shell was, of course, much smaller than that shell which would be fired from the great gun, but it was large enough to hold animals. Dr. Rhodes wished to see if the animals remained alive after the shell had been fired high into the air and had fallen back on to a sandy place such as might be hoped for on the moon.

"A dog was put into the shell. The gun was fired so that the shell came back to the earth on the sand north of Tampa. The top of the shell was removed; Dr. Rhodes looked inside. He carefully took hold of the dog; it was still alive, and had not been injured in any way. The experiment had been successful and Dr. Rhodes gave the signal to go ahead with the making of the big shell."

From "From Earth to Moon," by JULES VERNE.

(1) Who arranged the making of the
    shell? . . . .
(2) What animal was used for the
    experiment? . . . .
(3) Where did the shell come down? . . . .
(4) Was the experiment a success? . . . .
(5) Where did Dr. Rhodes eventually
    want his shell to go? . . . .

(C)

"That great cat, the leopard, can fight like a fury: and yet it often acts as a scavenger, devouring carrion some days old, even in districts of Africa and India where game is abundant. The lion prefers company but the leopard lives a solitary life. It is a creature of the night, and retires behing big rocks or in thick undergrowth at dawn. After it has fed on large game or sheep, this creature will carry the remains of the kill up a tree and hang it on a branch. It then knows that another meal awaits it on the following night. Audacious and cunning, the leopard will prowl round farms and villages after dusk. It will break into a kraal, then, with a sheep in its mouth, leap over a seven-foot palisade.

"The leopard is at home in every kind of country, whether it be the plains, rocky hills or thick equatorial forests. One African hunter wrote that the lion is a gentleman. But, he wrote, the leopard is the sneak of the animal world. One leopard in India killed more than two hundred human beings in two years. It is doubtful whether any man-eating tiger has as bad a record."

From "Mainly about Animals."

(1) At what time of day does the leopard hunt? ....

(2) Name two countries which the leopard inhabits. ....

(3) A leopard will often eat dogs. What other animal does it like to eat? ....

(4) Do you think that the leopard is a very strong animal? ....

(5) "Carrion" is decaying flesh. Do you think the leopard eats it? ....

(6) Which animal prefers not to be alone? ....

(7) Where does the leopard often hunt for its food? ....

(8) Where does the leopard often keep uneaten food? ....

(9) What does the word "abundant" mean? ....
The *opposite* of abundant is ....

(10) What does the word "audacious" mean? ....
The *opposite* of audacious is ....

EXERCISE 50(A)

(A) *Re-arrange each jumbled sentence:*—
flies where the in go time the do winter?
than careful better is it be sorry to?
kettle a never boils watched.
when think in doubt twice.
good makes fuel coal.

(B) *Select that word from the brackets which is related to the one given*:—

SWEET.   (ugly, cool, sugar, meat, pear).
PORTRAIT.   (gatepost, picture, harbour, health).
IRELAND.   (planet, town, train, island).
MISTAKE.   (foresee, discharge, error, steal).
WEAK.   (idle, feeble, big, wanted).

(C) *Complete these sentences with the correct words taken from the brackets*:—

Mr. Thomas .... well, for his boys rarely forgot what they .... from him. (learned, taught).

June .... very well but John had .... his work very carelessly. (wrote, written).

There was no doubt that the .... team won the match. (best, better).

(D) *What do we call*:—

trams, buses, carts, cars, and carriages? ....

a home with all the rooms on the ground floor? ....

geese, ducks, hens and turkeys? ....

sweets, candy and chocolate? ....

people chosen to sing together? ....

(E) *Supply a name for each of the following*:—

A hole made in the tyre of a bicycle. ....

The top of a hill or mountain. ....

The place from which a clergyman preaches ....

A place in which aeroplanes are kept. ....

Land surrounded by water. ....

A man who makes clothes. ....

A place where apples are grown. ....

Something which attracts iron. ....

(F) *Give* ONE *word for those words in italics*:—

The man ran *with great speed* for a doctor. ....

90

All of a sudden there was a deafening
   roar. . . . .
I shall be with you *in an instant.* . . . .
He *put off* his visit to the dentist. . . . .
The ship *came in sight* on the horizon. . . . .

(G) *Complete each sentence with the correct form of the word
      in brackets*:—
   John is the . . . . of the two boys. (tall).
   Fred is the . . . . writer in the school. (good).
   Of the two brothers, Peter is the . . . . (much).
      ambitious.
   Tom is the . . . . of the three boys. (strong).
   The careless girl produced the . . . .
      drawing in her class. (bad).

(H) *Find suitable "sound" words to complete the phrases*:—
   the . . . . of bells.   the . . . . of chains.
   the . . . . of water.   the . . . . of feet.
   the . . . . . of pens on paper.   the . . . . of hoofs.
   the . . . . of paper.   the . . . . of a crow.

(I) *From whom would you obtain the following?*—
   Fruit . . . .   Spectacles . . . .
   Hats . . . .   Flowers . . . .
   Sweets . . . .   Newspapers . . . .
   Prescriptions . . . .   Rings, brooches and
                                           bracelets . . . .

(J) *Where would you look to find*:—
   the address of a person? . . . .
   the position of a place? . . . .
   the meaning of a word? . . . .
   the day and date of the month? . . . .
   something which happened the
      previous day? . . . .

(K) *Insert the apostrophes*:—
   I havent time to catch the bus.
   Hed put the womans gloves in his pocket.
   The childrens clothes were put over the chair.

91

Jims car was much cleaner than Stephens.
"They'll be bringing Marys mother," John replied.

(L) *Correct the following sentences*:—
Both Jack and John was seen at the theatre.
Every one of us know that Thomas will win.
None of the prizes were very expensive.
Walk as quick as possible.
Neither Tom or I can swim.
I didn't know he was laying in bed.
He didn't believe nothing different to what his brother told him.
This end of the rope is the thickest.

(M) *Insert the capital letters and punctuate the following correctly*:—
tell me said the old gentleman what is your name i am mr johnson was the reply

(N) *Write down words* OPPOSITE *to*:—

private	horizontal . . . .
present	stationary . . . .
polite	guilty . . . .
danger	expand . . . .
optimist	condemn . . . .
free	freeze . . . .

(O) *Choose the correct word from the brackets*:—
The hunter went in pursuit (to, of) the animal.
He suffers (from, of) a swollen head.
I was sorry to part (of, with) that picture.
The girl complained (with, of) a sore throat.
The man disagreed (of, with) him.

(P) *Write down the* TWO *words that are* RELATED *in each group*:—
Orange, kidney, sunset, apple, tent.
Tree, help, helm, prod, leaf.
Glad, sad, mellow, happy, medium.
Paddle, swim, oar, book, boat.
Coal, corn, fuel, steel, brick.

(Q) *Make* NOUNS *from*:—

know ....   proud ....
weary ....   anxious ....

Make VERBS *from*:—

choice ....   decision ....
moisture ....   solution ....

Make ADJECTIVES *from*:—

attract ....   suspicion ....
notice ....   wisdom ....

(R) *Choose the correct word from the brackets*:—

My motor car had (it, his, its, it's) axle broken.

Nobody has (ever, never, sometimes, seldom) managed to
go to the moon in an aeroplane.

I (seen, saw, see, sawn) him yesterday evening.

He said, "Please give me (what, that, this, them) book over
there."

She is not nearly as tall as (his, him, he, her).

(S) *Complete the following*:—

We say, "As changeable as the .... "
What animal neighs? A ....
A .... was asked to solve the crime.
Every .... has a silver lining.
Birds of a feather .... together.
He was as patient as ....
A soldier posted to keep guard is called a ....
The past tense of "I think" is "I .... "
FELINE means "like a cat." What word means "like a
dog"? ....
"I eat an apple." The verb in this sentence is " .... "

(T) *Write down words which have the* SAME *or* NEARLY THE
SAME MEANING *as those given*:—

velocity ....   false ....
annually ....   solitary ....
manufacture ....   prohibit ....
meagre ....   pardon ....
mingle ....   authentic ....

93

(U) *Here are some everyday expressions. Choose the correct meaning from the brackets and indicate it by completing the sentence*:—

"TO MAKE SOMEONE'S MOUTH WATER" means (to make someone want something; to drink water; to hit someone in the face).

"TO SMELL A RAT" means (to know there is a rat in your house; to be suspicious of something; to smell something unpleasant).

"TO GIVE THE COLD SHOULDER TO SOMEONE" means (to duck someone in cold water; to ignore somebody; to leave the door open).

EXERCISE 50(B)

Read the following extracts and answer the questions beneath them by writing sentence answers:—

(A)

"Sam, Philip and Flo are school chums. Only Sam and Philip have bicycles. Philip and Flo are the only two who live in the town. Only Sam and Flo have sweets."—*Original.*

(1) Who has a bicycle and also lives in the town?

(2) Who lives in the town and has no sweets and rides a bicycle?

(3) Do any of the children living in the town have no sweets and do not ride a bicycle?

(4) Who lives in the country and has sweets?

(5) Who lives in the town, has sweets and has no bicycle?

(B)

"On Wednesday afternoon I went to the Public Library as usual to change my book. John, my friend, does not care for reading. He prefers to go for a swim with some of the boys in his class. The book I was returning was a very interesting one, all about life in the country. It was full of pictures of birds and wild flowers and country scenes. This time I thought I would choose a fiction book, perhaps a school story or a tale of adventure. These are my favourite kinds of reading. The library assistant in the Juvenile Section helped me to choose a book. It was called 'Adventures in the Andes'."—*Original.*

(1) On what day did I go to the Library? . . . .

(2) What is my friend's name? . . . .

(3) I went to the Library to (read; see my friend; change my book).

(4) John prefers to (walk; run; swim).

(5) Was the book I returned about school? ....

(6) Did I choose my book by myself? ....

(7) What was full of pictures? (the book at home; the book I took home; the book I returned).

(8) The word 'fiction' means — (imaginary; true; interesting).

(9) The word 'juvenile' means — (adult; young; adventure).

(10) How many times a week do I go to the Public Library?

(C)

"Drake was the most celebrated of the English 'Sea-dogs' of Queen Elizabeth's reign. He was born in Devonshire and grew up in a sea-faring atmosphere. He made three successful voyages to the New World, during which he plundered several Spanish settlements and made a daring march across the Isthmus of Panama, and in 1577 he set out on his famous voyage round the world in his ship the *Golden Hind*. He sailed through the Straits of Magellan, plundered Spanish settlements in Chile and Peru, captured treasure ships, claimed the coast of California in the name of his Queen, crossed the Indian and Pacific Oceans, sailed round the Cape of Good Hope, and finally returned to England in 1580, when he was knighted by Queen Elizabeth. In 1585 England went to war with Spain, and Drake won further honours leading a daring raid into the port of Cadiz. When the great Spanish Armada sailed up the English Channel in 1588, Drake played a chief part in the running fight, which lasted a week, before the Spaniards were finally driven off. Eight weeks later—on an expedition against the Spaniards in the West Indies—he was taken ill and died."

From "Teachers' World."

(1) Drake lived in the reign of (King Henry; Queen Elizabeth; Queen Anne). ......

(2) How many voyages did he make to the New World? ....

(3) He set out on his voyage round the world in (1477, 1577, 1947). ....

(4) What was the name of Drake's ship on this voyage? ....

95

(5) What were the Straits he sailed through? . . . .

(6) Name the Cape around which Drake sailed. . . . .

(7) Who knighted Drake on his return to England? . . . .

(8) In what year did England go to war with Spain? . . . .

(9) Against which port did Drake lead a daring raid? . . . .

(10) What sailed up the English Channel in 1588? . . . .

(11) How long did it take to repel the Spaniards? . . . .

(12) Where did Drake die? . . . .

(13) Who lived in Chile and Peru? . . . .

(14) Was Drake born in England? . . . .

(15) How many oceans are mentioned? . . . .